THE FUGITIVE FORESTER

Joel Robertson

Joel Robertson

THE FUGITIVE FORESTER

Joel Robertson

Published By:
Brentwood Publishers Group
4000 Beallwood Avenue
Columbus, Georgia 31904

CHAPTER I

Pete Lancaster was a man on a mission. It was a Sunday afternoon in late September. He was on the Ocmulgee River in central Georgia in an aluminum john boat with fishing tackle and quite a bit of extra gear. He had left his pickup truck on the bank of the river several miles upstream.

The purpose of this trip was to fake his death by drowning. He didn't want to pursue this course of action, but the alternative was jail after being framed for murder. He felt sure that given enough time he could prove his innocence. Faking death seemed to be the best way to buy time.

Pete fished as he drifted downstream. Although he liked to fish, catching fish wasn't foremost on his mind this trip. Fishing was just the cover up in case other fishermen, swimmers, etc. should remember seeing him. It was getting late in the day, and most people on the river for the weekend had left.

He had seen only two guys in a bass boat during the last mile on the river. He had two bass on a stringer that weighed about two pounds each. He had seen two bald eagles on this trip. They were definitely making a comeback.

Pete had decided he would fake an accident with the boat and drift several miles downstream in an inflatable raft he had brought along. He would then locate the motorcycle he had hidden earlier, and make his way during the night 120 miles to the southwest.

The distant roar of the rapids brought on the breeze from downstream jarred Pete's mind back to the business at hand. Around the next bend the rapids came into sight, and the roar of the river increased. The main stream of the river slipped to the right and tumbled over a granite ledge. Small islands separated the main stream from a broad expanse of river flowing choppily over broken granite. Before reaching the falls Pete beached the boat on one of the small, wooded islands, perhaps one half acre in size.

5

As he cleaned the fish, cooked them, and prepared an evening meal, his mind raced through the detailed plan he had formulated. As soon as he had eaten it was dark. He inflated the small rubber raft. He put all but a few items out of the boat being careful to leave his rod and reel as well as his tackle box. He put some essentials that he had brought along into a waterproof bag and tied it to the raft. He had extra clothes, sneakers, a few canned goods, fishing tackle and a .22 caliber single action pistol in a holster on his belt.

He launched the boat in the direction of the falls where it was sure to capsize. In the moonlight he launched the rubber raft and paddled toward the east side of the river where there was less turbulence. He needed to get about five more miles downstream where he had hidden a small Honda motorcycle. He heard a loud thump as the aluminum john boat tumbled over the falls and filled with water.

The current was swift, but the moon was shining bright and provided enough light so that Pete could see how to miss the rocks protruding above the surface. After a while he could see the granite foundation of Lamar's mill on the west bank rising 30 – 40 feet above the surface of the river. This mill, built before the civil war, used water power to grind grain until the 1940's when it was abandoned. The three story wooden structure that had formerly rested on the stone foundation had long ago disappeared.

Suddenly the current rapidly increased, and he heard some falls immediately ahead. He paddled frantically toward the east bank, but the current was too strong. He dropped about six feet in a deluge of water. The raft filled with water and soaked him, but he stayed afloat. Pete pulled the raft to the bank and dragged it to dry land. After emptying the water and drying off a bit he continued on down the river. Luckily he had tied all his items in the raft. From here on the water was relatively calm.

Another hour of drifting brought Pete to a small creek entering the river from the west. This is what he had been looking for. He beached the raft and deflated it. He then searched for the motorcycle he had hidden in a ditch nearby and covered with brush. He located the ditch, pulled out the motorcycle, and tied the deflated raft along with the bag of supplies onto the luggage rack. The motorcycle was a Honda 90 trail bike with a high and low range. This allowed speed on the highway and pulling power for navigating rough terrain.

The motorcycle had been hidden on land of Georgia Kraft Co., land owned by an industrial timber company – similar to Great Southern Timber Co. where Pete had worked. By the time the payload was secured it was approaching midnight. Pete had to go 120 miles and be well hidden before daylight.

He had made some elaborate preparations for survival during an extended stay in the woods. He had hidden all sorts of supplies – food, clothes, guns and ammunition, etc. in several choice locations. But it was all 120 miles away on the land he had previously managed, and where the boy was killed that Pete had been accused of murdering. He felt sure that given some time he could solve the mystery of who actually shot the boy.

The 120 mile trip would be through small towns, farm and forest land to land on the Alabama line just south of Columbus, Georgia. Here lay the large tracts of timberland which occupied primarily old farmland that had been abandoned when mechanized agriculture replaced animal power. The trip back and problems with remaining hidden didn't bother him too much. He thought he could pull it off. What really bothered him was the effect this would have on his sister Norma in Atlanta. She was 38 – ten years older than Pete. He had just spent a few days with her and her husband Larry and their two children before going fishing Sunday. He wanted very much to tell her of his plans, but he knew from experience, that if more than one person knows a secret it isn't a secret. It might be unintentional, but if she should let word slip out that Pete was still alive it would spoil all his plans, and only cause him more trouble and bring more criminal charges. The only choice was to keep his plans secret from everyone. She would no doubt be concerned when he didn't return from fishing. Her husband knew where he had gone fishing and would be looking for him by Monday morning. These were the thoughts going through his mind as he cranked the motorcycle and started out. The ride back to the Canyonlands Forest was uneventful as Pete expected it to be. Being careful not to exceed the speed limit and slowing way down when approaching towns he eased on through the night. The last thing he wanted was to attract attention to himself. After passing Forsyth on interstate 75 there was nothing but farms, forests, and very small towns. Rather than risk being stopped by inquisitive police in Forsyth he took rural roads that skirted the town. He had a tag on the motorcycle and a driver's license so there should be no problem in case he had his license checked. However, there was the remote possibility that a policeman would read in the paper about his drowning and remember that he checked a guy by that name on the night he supposedly drowned.

About two o'clock in the morning he passed a farm where farmers were gathering peanuts with a peanut combine. He could see a cloud of dust in the lights of the combine as it moved along the rows of peanuts that had been plowed up and inverted to dry. The combine picked up the vines, removed the peanuts, and dumped the vines back on the ground. When the cage on the combine that held about a ton of peanuts filled, they were dumped into an empty trailer. These guys must be running behind with their harvest to be working all night, Pete thought.

The cool night air and moonlight made for a very pleasant ride. About four in the morning he approached the rendezvous point with his supplies. Along highway 520 about ten miles south of Fort Benning was a patch of kudzu on private land that covered probably 50 acres. The kudzu, a vine imported from Southeast Asia, had been planted extensively in the past to control erosion. It did control erosion. However it didn't stop when the erosion was controlled. It grew like crazy and covered land and trees, turning the area into a vine covered jungle. It was a perfect hiding place. Pete turned off the motorcycle and listened. Not hearing or seeing any traffic he pushed the motorcycle off the road and it was soon swallowed by the kudzu patch.

CHAPTER II

Early Monday morning Norma awoke in Atlanta and looked out in the driveway for Pete's truck. It wasn't there. She woke Larry. "Larry, Pete's not back."

"Aw Norm", Larry responded, "He probably met some old gal or some buddies he spent the night with."

"I don't think so. I believe he would have called us. And what do you mean by the phrase 'some old gal'? You know Pete better than that. I'm worried that he must have had some trouble or he would have been back. Maybe you should go down there."

"I can't possibly go today", Larry responded. "Any other time I might take a day off, but today my boss from Chicago will be there. Anyway Pete will be back with a mess of fish to clean before long."

"I hope you're right", Norma said. "Well I've got to get these kids ready for school and go to work myself."

Late Monday afternoon after Larry got home from work, and Pete still wasn't back, Larry drove down to Jasper County, about 40 miles south of Atlanta. He checked out a public boat launching area where Pete usually put his boat in the river. Sure enough – there was Pete's pickup truck with no boat and no Pete. Pete's 12 foot aluminum boat was small and light. He didn't use an outboard motor and it really didn't require a trailer to transport it. He just loaded it into the bed of the pickup and piled his fishing tackle, boat paddle etc. in it. He really didn't need a boat ramp, and could put the boat in the river almost anywhere. However the public access area provided a good parking place and was very convenient.

At this point Larry began to really get concerned about Pete. It was getting very late in the day. Two guys were taking a bass boat out of the water and up the ramp on a trailer. Larry asked if they had seen Pete and described Pete's boat. One of them responded that they had launched their boat about noon time and that Pete's truck was there then, but no, they had not seen Pete or his boat. It would soon be dark, and Larry knew that it would be Tuesday before any search for Pete could begin so he drove back home.

That evening when Larry relayed to Norma what he had found out in Jasper County she was really upset.

"Well what are we going to do Larry?" she asked. "We have got to start a search for him somehow".

Larry called the Jasper County sheriff's office in Monticello and told them his problem. The sheriff wasn't there, but a deputy told him that the Game and Fish Commission would be far better equipped to start a search for Pete. He said the sheriff would be in about 8:00 in the morning. Larry then called the Game and Fish Commission at an office in Macon that was open all night. He was told that some game wardens would be at the Jasper County landing at 9:00 Tuesday morning. Larry and Norma then made some more calls to relatives, friends, etc. to make plans to be off work, get the kids to school, etc.

Tuesday morning found Norma and Larry, the Jasper County sheriff, and two game wardens along with a few fishermen and some family friends at the Jasper County boat landing. Of course Pete's truck was still there. The truck was still locked, but Larry knew where Pete had hidden an extra key in a magnetic box under the truck. Larry said that if Pete wasn't found they would take the truck home with them.

The game wardens were George and Norman. Both were in their 30's and looked very strong and capable. The wardens had a Dept. of Natural Resources boat which they used to patrol lakes and rivers. They were discussing where to search. It was only two miles upstream to the dam of Lake Jackson. The highway paralleled the calm river up to that point and it was pretty obvious that if Pete was on the river he would have gone downstream.

George, the game warden, spoke to the Jasper County sheriff, "You know the county line runs down the east bank of the river, not the middle. That puts the whole river and all the islands, etc. in Butts County."

The sheriff said, "Well I guess the Butts County sheriff sure needs to know about this. I'll see if I can get him on the radio." George said, "There is another boat ramp about 12 miles down the river. It's just below the shoals on the Jasper County side. You could go down there and look around and see if you see any sign of him." The wardens then launched their boat and took off down river.

As the day wore on a few fishermen came and went. The party waiting at the boat landing increased in size. A T.V. cameraman came and interviewed a few people. The Butts County sheriff showed up. The wardens came back after a couple of hours of fruitless searching. They had been talking to their office on the radio and two more wardens were launching a boat at the other boat ramp 12 miles south. The Butts County sheriff called the highway patrol and requested a helicopter to aid in the search. Word had spread to the fishermen and everyone by now, and everyone was looking for any trace of Pete. All had concluded that if Pete's problem was merely a disabled boat he could easily have walked out to a road or houses by now.

Larry went to Jackson to meet the highway patrol helicopter. The Butts County sheriff suggested that Larry go because he knew exactly what Pete's boat looked like. Larry met the chopper and they flew up and down the river just above the treetops for about an hour without seeing any trace of Pete's boat. They could see the river proper and the islands very well, but trees overhanging the river bank concealed a lot. At day's end, still with no trace of Pete or his boat, they all discontinued the search. Larry drove Pete's truck back to Atlanta as he and Norma returned home.

Early Wednesday morning Norma answered the phone and it was Lewis Everett from Milledgeville. He was a wood dealer who had some business association with Pete. He had shipped pulpwood to Great Southern paper mill at Cedar Springs, Georgia for a number of years. He had contracted to harvest timber off some of the land Pete managed. He knew Pete very well and had gone on Pete's bond when he was booked on the murder charge.

"What's the deal with Pete," Lewis asked Norma." I heard on the news last night that he was missing, and had been on a fishing trip in the river."

Norma replied, "Yes we were down there all day yesterday. His truck was there, but Pete and his boat can't be found. Everybody is looking for him. We brought his truck back up here last night. We are going back down there today. We've got to find him somewhere."

"Well I'll be down there too", Lewis said. "I don't know where this leaves me if he isn't found. You know I went his bond for $100,000."

"I know", said Norma, "I don't know what your obligation is either, but we are going to find him. We'll see you down at the river then."

Larry and Norma didn't arrive at the river in Jasper County until later in the morning on Wednesday. The Butts County sheriff, the same two game wardens, Lewis Everett, the wood dealer, and several others were there. Two fishermen were there and thought they had found Pete's boat. The way they described it Larry thought it probably was Pete's boat. The fishermen said it was almost on the bank on the Butts County side of the river about six miles downstream. They said they could go in on an old road that went to Lamar's mill and probably pull the boat to the bank and check it out.

The entire party left following the fishermen about ten miles around to the road going to the old mill site. There was a locked gate on the road that had once been a county road. At a house close to the gate the game wardens obtained a key to the gate. The party then proceeded to the river. The fishermen led them upstream. They came to a place where the river tumbled over several ledges of broken granite. A series of minor waterfalls three to ten feet high stretched across the river. It was the power of the falling water that had been harnessed originally to power the grist mill. Many years ago in addition to the grist mill there had been a cotton gin, cotton spinning mill, and a sawmill at this location – all powered by the falling water.

12

The fishermen were leading the way along the river bank when they stopped between some boulders and pointed out the boat. The roar from the rapids was powerful. It was difficult to hear each other talk. The boat had gone over about a six foot waterfall, filled with water and partially sunk with only a couple feet of the bow above the water and resting against another rock. The fishermen, game wardens, and Larry waded out and looked at it.

Larry said, "Yep that's Pete's boat alright."

They grabbed the boat, struggling to free it from the water and rocks, and began to work it to the bank. Trees were overhanging the site preventing it from being seen from the air the day before. One of the game wardens picked up a rod and reel in the shallow water. Larry said it belonged to Pete. Once they got the boat to the bank they began to wade the water and crawl around on the rocks looking for any sign of Pete. Larry told them that he just couldn't believe Pete had drowned because he always wore a life vest.

Norman Allrich, one of the game wardens, said, "Well he could have hit his head on a rock when the boat turned over, or something like that. There was a guy in a canoe that drowned a few years ago in this same part of the river. The canoe dumped him in fast water, he went barely under the water and his life preserver harness hung on a snag. The fast current held him under until he drowned. We were lucky to have found his body. If he hadn't had on a life preserver he probably would have been alright. You never know."

It was becoming obvious that if Pete was to be found it would be his body. At this point no one believed he would be found alive. Lewis Everett, the wood dealer, was most concerned. He said, "If we don't find his body to prove he is dead, I wonder if they will make me pay the bond money?" No one in this group could answer his question. The game wardens called the other natural resource personnel who were searching the river farther downstream and told them about finding the boat. They planned to concentrate their search tomorrow in the area where the boat was found. Larry and Norma headed back to Atlanta with heavy hearts.

13

CHAPTER III

Jeff Callahan was a millionaire banker who controlled a lot of timberland. He had inherited the land and plenty of money. He was used to having everything his way. He was about 55 years old, and stood about five feet ten inches tall. He had grey hair with a little baldness showing, bushy eyebrows protruded over deep-set grey eyes which shifted as he talked. He wore red suspenders, cowboy boots and carried a nine millimeter Luger pistol which he swore to the gods above had belonged to Rommel, the famous German general of World War II. In fact he swore all the time about everything. He mostly swore about his fellow man however. To anyone who happened to be near he told what a sorry lot the rest of humanity was. Deep down he thought everyone envied him and was out to "get" him. His goal in life seemed to be to "get" the other man first.

Whitetail deer had become extinct throughout central Georgia and Alabama in the late 1800's due to subsistence hunting. In an effort to reintroduce deer in the area a restocking program was started shortly after World War II. The 200,000 acre military reservation at Ft. Benning was a natural site for restocking efforts. Callahan's land along with timber company land south of Ft. Benning was signed up as part of the wildlife refuge. The state refuge extended about ten miles south of Ft. Benning and eight miles east and west. It encompassed 50,000 acres. The Chattahoochee River which is the Georgia-Alabama line formed the western boundary of the refuge. Deer were live trapped and relocated to the wildlife refuges from Wisconsin, Texas, islands off the Georgia coast, or wherever healthy populations of deer could be found. Game wardens patrolled the refuges to protect the deer from illegal hunting.

In a few years deer were making a marvelous comeback on land that had been abandoned for farming. Row crop farming had failed in many areas of the southeast for various reasons. Once mechanization started replacing animal power on the farms, the steep land that couldn't be farmed mechanically was gradually abandoned. The farmers sold the land to timber companies or speculators and moved away. Some people moved to flatter land that could be farmed with tractors and machinery, but most gave up farming and moved to the cities.

As an example of the decline in farming, Stewart County, which bordered the Georgia side of the Chattahoochee River immediately south of Ft. Benning has a land area of 289,000 acres. In 1900 there were 244,000 acres in farmland, and the population was 15,856. By 2000 there were only 27,500 acres in farmland, and the population was 5,145. In 100 years the county had gained 216,500 acres of timberland. It had gone from 16 percent timberland to 91 percent timberland. The land still being farmed was the wide, fertile river bottoms and some of the more level, fertile land farther inland from the river.

The refuge which joined Ft. Benning on the south was about fifteen miles south of Columbus, Ga. Mr. Callahan's dad had enough money to buy up the land as it was abandoned in the 1920's and 1930's. Most of the land was purchased for less than five dollars per acre. Mr. Callahan's land joined by other timberland holdings extended another six or seven miles downstream, and then the farmland started.

Fort Benning, the huge army infantry base lying immediately north of the refuge extended all the way to Columbus. It was nearly two hundred thousand acres and extended across the river into Alabama. The base was created in the 1920's by the government condemning the land through the power of eminent domain. The farm families were moved to other locations.

In addition to putting the land in the game preserve Mr. Callahan had also entered a long term lease with Great Southern Paper Co. Great Southern managed the land for timber production. It became part of the Canyonlands Forest that Pete Lancaster, one of Great Southern's foresters had been managing.

Jeff Callahan had been instrumental in helping the state of Georgia get the land from various ownerships signed up in the game preserve. In return, the game and fish commission tried

15

every way to please him. Joe Scholski was a state game warden on the fifty thousand acre game preserve which included the land belonging to Jeff. Joe was a middle-aged man, very stout, with black hair. Joe had been told by Jeff to hide on the public road that ran through the property and shoot Allen King in the leg. Allen was a local playboy who was shining deer on the place at night and shooting them just for the fun of it. Jeff thought that would be a good way to stop the poaching. Joe wouldn't do it so Jeff had Joe put him out and pick him up later. Jeff had hidden in the woods beside the road. A car came along slowly shining a light then stopped and someone fired. This was at a known deer crossing. Jeff crawled through the brush intending to shoot Allen in the legs. Instead of Allen it was two strangers. One was at the fallen deer on the other side of the road. Another guy was at the car. The one at the car heard Jeff in the bushes and raised a gun. Jeff instinctively shot quickly with his Luger. It was more or less a reflex response to seeing the gun pointed in his direction. He ran back through the bushes. The man at the deer didn't see him. Jeff didn't know it then, but his one quick shot had dead centered the boy's chest.

Jeff ran back through the woods to the rendezvous point and waited for Joe to pick him up. Then he began to think and worry about the situation he had just been in. What if he had killed the boy he shot? Then he thought about the pistol. Maybe he should get rid of it in case problems developed. Where could he hide it? He decided to hide it in the loft of an old, dilapidated farm building nearby. The old house was built with pine logs and had a wood shingle roof originally which had been replaced with a metal roof at a much later date. The metal roof had protected the building for many years although it was very rusty now. The house had a native stone fireplace. The front porch had fallen in and vines covered much of the house.

Jeff scampered into the attic and placed the pistol under some old wooden shingles behind the chimney. The shingles had fallen to the floor of the attic most likely when the original roof was replaced. His plan was to pick up the pistol later. After hiding the pistol he headed to the rendezvous point to meet Joe. Later Joe picked Jeff up in his game warden truck and they headed to Columbus.

Joe said, "I heard some shots. What happened?' Jeff lied and said, "I don't know. It was on beyond me and sounded like two different guns. There was some hollering and too many people. I decided I better get the hell out of there. I lost my damn Luger on the way back too. I'll look for it sometime when things calm down."

A stroke of luck for Jeff was that Pete came upon the car in his truck a few minutes later. The district judge's boy was dead and a local schoolteacher's boy was trying to get him in the car to go to the hospital. Pete helped get the boy in the car and sped off to the nearest hospital in Columbus about 15 miles away where he was pronounced dead. Pete had had trouble with Glen before. When they were at the hospital Glen told the sheriff that he thought Pete did the shooting then came along later acting innocent. Pete had owned a nine millimeter P-38 pistol, but it had been stolen from his truck earlier that year. He had reported the theft to the Stewart County sheriff. They questioned Pete but couldn't find enough evidence to prosecute him.

Judge Smith, the father of the boy who was killed, applied a lot of pressure to the law enforcement people to solve the boy's murder. He later got with Glen Alrich and they came up with more "evidence" that Pete shot his son. They built a strong case against Pete. Pete had been out riding around and can't establish being any place else at the time of the shooting. After a lot of pressure from Judge Smith a warrant was finally issued for Pete's arrest. Pete was booked for murder and bond was set at $100,000. Pete called on a friend and business associate, a wood dealer named Lewis Everett at Milledgeville, Ga.

Mr. Everett was a middle aged man who had a successful business buying and shipping pulpwood to various paper mills in the Southeast. Pete had done business with him. Mr. Everett thought a lot of Pete and was glad to go his bond. He knew Pete wasn't guilty of murder and wanted to help him however he could.

17

When the circumstances of Jessie Smith, the judge's boy, being killed, pointed more and more to Pete Lancaster as the murderer, Pete knew he had to do something. He made up his mind that he wasn't going to jail for something he didn't do. He made some elaborate plans to fake his death then hide and survive in the woods until he could come up with hard evidence that he was not the murderer.

The canyon Pete picked for his primary hiding place was about one quarter mile long. It was 150 feet deep where it started abruptly on a hillside. It had a small stream in the bottom due to the fact that the canyon had eroded down to the water table. Unlike most of the canyons however, this one had a small cave in some limestone that protruded from the canyon wall.

Pete's motorcycle was painted camouflage colors so it was very easy to hide in the kudzu patch. From that point he walked about two miles west toward a canyon on the Canyonlands Forest. A slit in the side of the canyon was a cave in limestone rock that had been exposed by the erosion. He had found it while cruising timber several years ago. It was well stocked and the entrance was well hidden. It had been a long day and night for Pete. He was extremely tired and sleep was long overdue. It was almost daybreak. He had been on the go for almost twenty-four hours straight. He crawled into the cave and immediately fell asleep.

Like most of the canyons that formed in this area, the soil type that so enhanced canyon formation was made up of six to eight feet of clay overlaying various depths of coarse sand. The land was settled and cleared for agriculture soon after the Indians were removed in the 1820's. A lot of the steep hillsides were cleared of timber, the soil was plowed with mules and oxen to grow cotton. Erosion was sudden and fast. If a gully penetrated the top layer of loam and clay the water then hit the sand below and it melted like a sand castle on the beach. In a very few years the harsh winter rains falling on unprotected soil turned many farms into a series of gullies and canyons. By the early 1900's much of the land was being abandoned. Pine seed, born on the wind, was quick to turn the abandoned fields into pine forests.

This slowed the runoff of rainwater, but many of the canyons, once formed, continued to grow. The one area where the clay-sand soil type predominated, and canyons were so prevalent was about fifteen miles north and south and fifteen miles east and west lying south of Fort Benning, Georgia.

Another hiding place Pete had stocked was a small hill, covering about an acre, that rose twenty feet above the water level of a large complex of beaver ponds. The beaver ponds covered about one hundred acres in a creek bottom adjacent to the Chattahoochee River. The little hill was in the middle of beaver ponds and was reached by wading. Pete had hidden a canoe in a vine covered ditch near the river, and on the hill in the beaver pond nearby he had hidden groceries, a shotgun, and a rifle along with traps, fishing equipment, etc.

When Pete woke after sleeping nearly all day he started focusing on his plans for survival. He was prepared to stay a long time if it became necessary. He hoped he could find some evidence to support his story and make a quick exit from hiding, but he didn't know. With the motorcycle he could travel on the roads if he had to, but he ran the risk of being recognized. Travel in and out of the cave area could be hidden by walking in the water of the small stream below and leaving and entering the stream at various points so a path wasn't created. By using the canoe he could travel up and down the river or cross it into Alabama.

Pete was fairly certain at this point that his plan had gone well. He was safe in a territory that he was intimately familiar with. He had the supplies and the ability to renew them from the farms, forests, and waters of the surrounding area. Most of the time there was no one in the vast tracts of timberland in the surrounding area except a few loggers, tree planters, timber cruisers, etc. This was especially true during the long, hot, summers. The deer season was rapidly approaching however, and this would bring hoards of people from the cities of Georgia and Florida to deer camps scattered throughout the woods.

The cave he had found and stocked was on land that was open for public hunting by purchasing a permit. Pete had a permit, hunting license, etc., but he sure didn't want to run the risk of having his permit checked and someone locally recognizing him. Also, he knew that the more he remained in the area of the cave the more likely it was that some hunter would see him coming and going. He was afraid this would lead to someone discovering the cave. He had covered the cave entrance with camouflage netting. A natural growth of vines covered the whole wall of the canyon. A person would almost have to step into the cave entrance to know it was there. The entrance was about thirty feet above the stream at the bottom of the canyon. By walking on rocks from the stream up to the entrance he could go and come without leaving a trace. But still, if someone saw him going and coming they might discover the cave.

The other hideout, on the hill in the beaver ponds, was 20 miles away in the 50,000 acre wildlife refuge joining Fort Benning. There would be no hunters there who might detect his movements. The perimeter of the refuge was checked by game wardens, and the road through the refuge to the boat launching area on the river was patrolled by game wardens. This is the road where Jessie Smith was killed. Once in the interior of the refuge he would remain safe from detection by the casual hunter. By carefully entering and leaving the refuge on foot or with the canoe Pete knew he had a better chance of remaining undetected. After a few days in the cave area he decided to leave the motorcycle where it was hidden in the kudzu patch, pack some supplies on a packboard and head for the hill in the beaver ponds near the river.

It was late September. The deer season opened in about three weeks. In the meantime hunters would be prospecting the possibilities by locating deer trails, feeding areas, etc., and preparing deer stands. The weekends would be especially busy with these activities in the area where he was now. Some of the people seeking outdoor recreation who boated and fished on the river then hunted during the winter would be abandoning the river now to prepare for deer hunting. This would diminish boat traffic on the river and possibly make any excursions by canoe on the river less likely to be noticed.

It was almost sundown when Pete left the cave with a packboard full of supplies. He was dressed in camouflage and carried a .22 caliber pistol, a .243 rifle and a flashlight. The first cool front of the year had swept in from the northwest the night before. There would be no more hot, muggy, days. The crisp fall air had arrived. The yellow poplar, sweetgum, red maple, scarlet oak, and colorful vines and shrubs were beginning to really show their colors. They would reach their peak later in October. As the daylight faded Pete traveled the trails and back roads into the night on a twenty mile hike toward the west and the hill in the beaver ponds. A screech owl made his long, wavering call and occasionally the big guns at Ft. Benning sounded like distant thunder as Pete hiked through the night.

Chapter IV

After the game wardens, sheriff deputies, etc had searched for Pete's body four days unsuccessfully they decided to give up the search. George Daniel and Norman Allrich who had been on the search from the beginning, were convinced that a body would not be found.

George said, "Norman, I am beginning to wonder if Pete Lancaster really drowned in this river."

Norman said, "Well if he's not here in the river, where is he? Where else could he be? You know, sometimes a body will show up a month or more after a drowning. If he is hung under a rock somewhere the gators and turtles could finish him off."

" I don't know about gators", said George. "I saw a small one up this far north one time, but I guess turtles and catfish could do away with a body. Of course if he is hung under a rock someplace we are never going to find him anyway. I know one thing. We have a lot of other things to do. The boss says to wrap this up. So I guess we quit looking."

"Yeah let's load up and get down to Macon."

Norma and Larry were in Gus Bloomdale's law office in Atlanta. It had been two weeks since Pete disappeared. Norma and Larry had known Gus since their high school days. Of course Gus had known Pete very well also. It was only natural that Pete had consulted him, as well as a local lawyer in Columbus, when he was accused of killing Jessie Smith.

Norma said, "Gus, what can we do? It is obvious they aren't going to find Pete's body."

"Well Norma you really can't do anything." Gus said. "After a year if no trace of him ever shows up we can declare him legally dead and settle his estate. In the meantime you can't sell any of his assets, collect insurance, or anything. Do you know if he had a will?"

"Yes, I know he had one. He had a safe deposit box at the bank in Lumpkin. His will is probably in that box. What about his truck? What can we do with that?"

Gus said, "You can take it and use it. When it comes time to buy a tag, just buy a tag for the truck, but you can't take title to it until the estate is settled. Have you ever considered the fact that Pete might have faked his death?"

"Yes, I thought about it, but I discounted it as soon as it came to my mind. In the first place he would have told me about such a plan, and he never would have left his truck and so many personal things. He would have made some arrangements."

"O.K., it was just a thought. Such things have happened. You never know."

"Lewis Everitt called me." Gus said, "He was wondering about the bond he had signed for. Lewis pledged a bank C.D. for the bond. He is going to be required to put up the $100,000 cash until Pete is declared legally dead."

When Pete reached the beaver ponds it was about 2:A.M. He had earlier picked a route through the shallow water to the hill hidden in the complex of beaver ponds. It had been quite a while since he was there, and in the dark he couldn't be sure of the route. He didn't want to step off in a deep hole with a pack on his back, nor did he want to meet a cottonmouth moccasin, so he decided to sleep until daybreak.

The complex of beaver ponds had formed where two small streams merged in a valley. When the beavers dammed the streams in this flat bottom land the water spread out and covered many acres. A series of dams progressed upstream for over a mile. Many of the flooded trees in the creek bottom had died. A mixture of live trees, dead trees, vines, etc. hid the small hill that Pete had found out in the middle of the vast complex. From where the beaver dams ended it was about 300 yards downstream to the Chattahoochee River. Just off the river in a vine covered ditch Pete had hidden his canoe.

When Pete woke it was daylight. He shouldered the packboard, picked up his rifle and waded to the hill in the middle of the beaver ponds. It was just as he had left it a month ago. He retrieved some of the waterproof bags that he had hidden with a tent, sleeping bag, groceries, fishing tackle, etc. He erected the tent which had a camouflage pattern on it. The hill was covered with trees, and the tent blended into the local cover very well. It also had mosquito netting which was very important.

From this location he could hear motorboats on the river. On weekends fishermen created quite a bit of boat traffic. During the week there was very little boat traffic. There were fish in the beaver ponds, and Pete thought he could catch all he needed to eat in the ponds without exposing himself to possible discovery on the river. He had a fish trap made with small mesh wire. It was about four feet long and eighteen inches in diameter. He baited this with some canned meat and set it in the channel of the stream.

He decided that during the coming night he would paddle the canoe about two miles downstream and see what kind of food he might find on some of the farms. He was dressed in camouflage and carried some burlap bags as well as a flashlight, pistol, and a few cans of food. Late in the day he waded the pond to shore and proceeded downstream to the hidden canoe.

It was time now to make some definite plans for survival. Pete didn't know how long he would have to remain hidden, but he knew he should prepare for the worst. The most immediate concern was food. He had stored guns, ammo, clothes, traps, and food-both dried and canned. This needed to be augmented by adding variety. It was harvest time on the farms on both sides of the river downstream. Besides huge fields of cotton, farmers were gathering peanuts, corn, soybeans, and to a lesser extent, sweet potatoes, apples, watermelons, etc.

It was almost dark when Pete reached the canoe. He dragged it out from under the vines in the ditch and launched it into the small creek then paddled into the river. The canoe was twelve feet long made by the Old Town Canoe Co. in Old Town, Maine. It was colored green. It was made from a very tough fiberglass-like material that could withstand a lot of rough treatment. Pete had stored two paddles, a life preserver, and a jungle hammock in the canoe.

There was no boat traffic on the river now, and it was totally dark except for some stars and a weak moon. It is surprising how well you can see when you gradually get used to the darkness. There was some risk of being discovered on the river, but Pete decided it was very minimal, and if he stayed close to the bank he could disembark and snatch the canoe out of the water if he saw lights or heard a motorboat coming.

The Chattahoochee River at this point was actually a lake, so there was very little current. A lock and dam downstream at Ft. Gaines, Georgia, built by the Corps of Engineers, backed the water sixty miles to Columbus, Georgia. The river dropped about one foot per mile. At this point, fifteen miles south of Columbus, the river remained within its original banks. Tugboats and barges operated on the river to a limited extent from Apalachicola, Florida to Columbus, Georgia. Columbus was the northern terminal of river navigation. River shipping terminates at Columbus because of shoals in the river.

Paddling the light canoe in the moonlight, Pete made good time and soon came to the farmland. The very productive farms stretched for miles downstream on both sides of the river at this point. There were large fields of all kinds of crops. Pete's primary objective was obtaining a food supply that was easily transported, and that would last for a long time without refrigeration.

He beached the canoe where a small stream ran into the river through a deep gully. He pulled the canoe upstream out of sight before climbing the bank and looking out over a big peanut field that had just been harvested. He went back to the canoe and retrieved the jungle hammock, stretched it between two trees, and crawled in for some sleep before daylight.

The hammock was army surplus. It had a canvas roof and mosquito netting on the sides with a long zipper for access. It was very comfortable, and kept a person off the ground while furnishing protection from rain and insects. Pete slept until daylight. He then took down the hammock and put it back in the canoe.

After eating some canned sausage and wild grapes he took two of the burlap bags and his backpack, climbed up to the woods surrounding the peanut field and remained alert for human activity. Away across the level, bottomland field he could see a few

25

wild hogs feeding on peanuts spilled or left in the ground during the harvesting process. He would like to get a wild hog, but that would have to come later. He didn't have a rifle with him, and would not have risked the sound of a rifle shot at this location.

At periodic intervals along the edges of the field were small piles of peanuts about eight or ten inches tall. This was where the peanut combine had malfunctioned and spilled peanuts. The farmers were dealing with peanuts by the ton. They didn't have time to pick up the many little piles of spilled peanuts. Pete quickly filled the two sacks with peanuts and took them back to the canoe.

As the morning wore on the valley became alive with the noise of giant machines harvesting peanuts, corn, cotton, and soybeans farther down the valley. A couple of miles farther down river smoke and steam erupted with a dull roar from a huge paper mill on the west bank of the river in Alabama. A train trestle crossed the river at that point.

At a corn field that had just been harvested there were ears of corn on the ground that had been missed by the corn picker. Pete had anticipated gleaning these spilled ears of corn, but then he saw a steel wagon with tons of shelled corn parked at the end of the field and waiting to be towed to a grain bin. Pete climbed into the wagon and scooped about forty pounds of shelled corn into a sack. He quickly stowed this in the canoe.

At an orchard he filled his backpack with apples and pears. He also found a watermelon patch, carried a watermelon into the woods, ate it and hid the rinds. There were some big pecan orchards, but the pecans were not ready yet. They would have to wait until later.

Periodically boats were traversing the river, but this slowed when darkness came. In the darkness Pete dragged the canoe laden with corn, peanuts, apples, and pears down the small stream, launched it into the river, and started the return trip upriver to the beaver ponds and his hideout. The trip had gone smoothly so far. He hadn't seen anyone close by and was fairly certain no one had seen him. He couldn't help but wonder how long he would have to live the life of a fugitive before he could produce some compelling evidence that he was not responsible for the death of Jessie Smith.

As Pete paddled the canoe upriver in the darkness, deep in thought about his predicament in life, he was suddenly aware of a deep, rumbling sound from down river. At first he thought it was a freight train crossing the trestle near the paper mill. Suddenly he realized it was much closer than he thought. A bright light came around a bend behind him and it seemed that the whole width of the river was taken up by a tugboat pushing a big barge. It was making big time and suddenly bearing down on him. Pete dug in the paddle and promptly hugged the eastern river bank, which at this point was quite steep. All he could do was hope for the best. When the tugboat went churning noisily by a huge wave hit the canoe and almost turned it over. The canoe dipped and took on some water, but Pete managed to keep it upright and promptly bailed out the water. About twenty minutes later he made it to the stream flowing from the beaver ponds.

Pete hid the canoe then slept a while in the jungle hammock. At daylight he began packing the food back to the hill in the swamp. With the food safely stowed he went to check the fish trap. It held three catfish of one to two pounds each and a few bream. He cleaned and dressed the fish then built a small fire and roasted them.

Laying in supplies before deer season opened and the woods filled with hunters was Pete's only goal. It was the driving force that commanded his full attention day and night. He roasted the dry corn in an iron skillet over hot coals making what the American Indians called pinole. They used this as winter food or trail food. It was light, easy to carry, and lasted for months when kept dry. He also smoke cured some fish.

The apples and pears were cut into thin slices which were laid on a canvas until dried. It took several days to dry them this way. They had to be protected from the rain, raccoons, etc. If it rained, the canvas containing the fruit was stored inside the tent. When the sun shined, the canvas, spread on the ground, soon reached a high temperature which dried the fruit. The dried and smoked food was then stored in five gallon buckets with tight fitting lids. The buckets were then stored underground. The sweet potatoes were buried in holes dug in the ground and lined with pine boughs.

With these projects completed Pete turned his thoughts to larger game. Deer were very plentiful now – especially on the refuge where he was located. No hunting was allowed here. Very limited hunting was allowed on the 200,000 acre military reservation lying immediately to the north. Wild hogs were fairly plentiful, especially around the big peanut fields he had just visited.

The hogs were easy to trap. He had done it before. He had built a pen of logs, boards , or wire about eight feet square and six feet high. The pen had a sliding door that fit into grooves on both sides of the door. The door was raised and held up by a rope which ran through a pulley above the door. The rope then was tied to a stick which was pegged to the ground in the rear of the pen. The trap was then baited with corn which was spread liberally around the bait stick. When a hog rooted the bait stick out of the way the door would fall trapping whatever hogs were in the pen. Sometimes five or six hogs would be in the pen when the door fell.

Pete was sure the farmers would be glad for him to trap the hogs. Farmers had encouraged hunters to shoot and trap the hogs in the past. One farmer told Pete how he had stood on a hill overlooking the bottomland and witnessed four different categories of "varmints" eating his green peanuts at the same time. The deer were eating the vines and pawing the green peanuts out of the ground. The hogs were rooting them up. Turkeys were scratching them up, and beavers were climbing out of the river to dig them up.

There was only one thing wrong with building a trap pen. It was something that could not be hidden. No matter if it was built on farmland, the refuge, or Ft. Benning, it stood a good chance of being discovered by someone. If someone found it, it remained a simple matter for them to watch it and catch whoever was attending the trap. For this reason, Pete ruled out the possibility of a hog trap. He reasoned that he could sneak into a feeding area and shoot one in the head with a .22 rifle without causing much attention. He decided to wait until the onset of winter to try this however. He needed cold weather to salt cure the meat. He wasn't sure he could dry pork like he could deer. The deer could be cut into thin strips and dried over the fire to make jerky.

Pete had a few wire snares he planned to set for deer. They were small cables, about 1/5 inch in diameter with a one way sliding lock. The loose end was securely fastened to a tree or something solid. The end with the sliding lock was formed into a noose and placed in a deer trail where the vegetation naturally guided the deer's head into the noose. As the deer pressed forward the noose would tighten around the deer's neck and choke it to death.

Variations of this technique had been used by men for millennia with nooses made of rawhide or sinew. The advantage here was silence. Pete had used snares in trapping beaver and otter. He was sure they could be used on deer although he had never tried them on deer.

There are several advantages to trapping animals, birds, and fish as opposed to sport hunting and fishing. Traps can be set in many locations and they work around the clock. The traps are silent, and at this time silence was very important to Pete. He had a crossbow which was silent and very powerful, but it was back at the cave. Traps and snares were illegal for game animals, but they were certainly efficient. Pete had trapped furbearers for profit ever since high school, so he had a good knowledge of the art of trapping. The disadvantage of trapping is that the traps or a trapped animal might be spotted by someone. If a game warden spotted his trap and waited to see who visited it, it could be curtains for Pete. He knew he would have to use caution.

There was a big kudzu patch not far from the beaver ponds. Pete thought this would be a good place to try the snares for deer. When he left the hill and waded the beaver pond he always took a little different route. The purpose of this was to keep from establishing a trail of muddy footprints that someone might notice. After stashing the hip boots and donning a pair of army jungle boots Pete proceeded to the kudzu patch with three snares to set for deer.

The kudzu was a vine brought to the U.S. from Southeast Asia in the early 1900's. It was planted on eroded land, railroad embankments, etc. to stop erosion. The rapidly growing vine with deeply penetrating roots would rapidly establish a vegetative cover on bare land. Vines would grow as much as thirty feet per year. The problem started when the vine had established a cover on the eroded area and kept on growing. Expanding at the rate of twenty percent per year, the vines soon covered trees, houses, or whatever was in its path. Some of the patches first established in the 1930's by the Civilian Conservation Corps now covered 100 acres or more creating a veritable jungle. Some attempts were made to control the vine with herbicides, but it was a slow go and very expensive.

The vine was very nutritious to grazing animals. It was as high in protein as alfalfa . For this reason the deer and cattle loved it. In fact, cattle grazing was one means of controlling the plant. The only thing feeding on the kudzu Pete was in now however was deer. They had trails at intervals through the vines. These trails afforded excellent opportunities to capture a deer with a snare. It was also highly unlikely that anyone would ever see it. People didn't walk through kudzu without a very good reason. Three snares were set. The center of a 24 inch loop was placed about 30 inches above the ground in narrow spots along trails. The kudzu vines well camouflaged the snares.

With the snares set, Pete retraced his steps back to the beaver pond. The yellow poplar and red maple trees were really beginning to show their colors now. It was the second week of October. A breeze from the north brought cooler air and the noise of big guns at Ft. Benning. Occasionally a transport plane would drop paratroopers in training on the Alabama side of the river at Ft. Benning. Pete thought that with all the noise made by the military maneuvers he probably could just shoot a deer, and no one would hear it. But, he thought, why take that chance when it wasn't necessary. He checked the fish trap on the way back to the hill. It produced a few more catfish and bream.

Next morning upon checking the snares he found that he had snared a medium size doe. He gutted and skinned the doe, then set to work cutting all the meat from the bones. He planned to cook a little of the fresh meat and make jerky out of most of it. When he finished this task he had about fifty pounds of pure meat. He removed the other two snares, loaded all the meat on a pack frame, and made his way back to the hill in the beaver ponds.

With all this meat to smoke he needed a secure frame to hang the meat on. He remembered seeing some old junk farm equipment close by that had been left over from earlier times when the land was in agriculture instead of trees. Upon exploring this junk for something useful he suddenly felt a tug on his pants leg as something pricked the skin of his leg. He thought it was a briar, but upon glancing downward saw that a snake had struck at him and hung its fangs in Pete's pants leg. Pete quickly knocked the snake loose and killed it with a stick he had in his hand. The snake was a copperhead moccasin about three and a half feet long. The fangs had merely scraped across the skin, but did not penetrate. Yellow venom was on the surface of Pete's leg. He had been very lucky. If all that venom had penetrated his leg it could have been the end. It certainly would have been the end of his hiding out. This really gave Pete a scare. Killing the snake was a reflex action, but now reality set in and the more he thought about it the more scared he became. He immediately swore that until the weather got cold he would wear his snake leggings at all times. With shaking hands he managed to take a wheel off an old horse drawn hay rake. The big, iron wheel was about five feet in diameter with many iron spokes. Pete thought that this wheel suspended above a bed of coals would be ideal for smoking fish and making jerky. He got the wheel back to the hill by a combination of rolling and carrying it.

A fire was started with oak and hickory. While this was burning to produce a bed of coals Pete sliced the venison into thin strips. The wheel was arranged in a horizontal position, and the strips of venison were suspended over the spokes of the wheel. After the fire produced good, hot coals these were shoveled under the wheel. In about eight hours all the moisture was gone from the meat. Pete then had a product that would last for months. The fifty pounds of venison produced about twenty pounds of jerky.

CHAPTER V

Pete decided to take some of the roasted corn and jerky to the cave and stash it away before deer season started. The pack frame was loaded with corn and jerky, and as he prepared to make the 20 mile hike back to the cave he thought about a canyon about one half the distance between the two hideouts. He had been thinking about what a great place it would be to lose someone in case he was being pursued and needed to make a quick getaway. He packed a 200 foot nylon rope in a plastic bag that he planned to hide somewhere around the head of the canyon. He had thought about doing this before, while he was hiding supplies, but just never got around to it.

Late in the day, as the sun was setting, Pete started back east toward the cave. He pulled the fish trap out of the water as he was leaving. He was wearing camouflage as usual, and wore snake leggings and ten inch leather boots. He carried the pack frame loaded with corn and jerky as well as the rope, poncho, and a few other items. He wore a camouflage cap and carried a .22 pistol and a small flashlight. A canteen was on his belt and he carried a four foot stick. As darkness came on he walked the road running east that split the game refuge. This road led to the boat landing and picnic area on the river. It was the same road where he came upon Jessie Smith dying from a bullet through the chest. It was the event that led to his situation now.

Who would have believed that trying to help someone could have resulted in so much pain and misery? And who was the person who shot the judge's boy? When Glen Alrich who was at the downed deer heard the shot that killed Jessie he turned around and saw no one. It was dark and the assailant had fired from the cover of the woods on the other side of the road. Detectives found the nine millimeter bullet that passed through Jessie and lodged inside the car. They had looked for a shell casing and footprints in the area where the assailant was standing. The ground was covered with straw and grass in that area. In the trampled grass they found the shell casing.

Because this was the judge's boy who had been killed, the pressure was intense to find the killer. The sheriff and the G.B.I. had worked night and day. Glen Alrich had known Pete for some time. He knew Pete had a 9MM pistol. However he didn't know it had been stolen. He theorized that Pete had parked his truck somewhere and snuck in to guard the deer crossing. After telling the G.B.I. and sheriff this theory they grabbed it wholeheartedly. At least the G.B.I. did. The sheriff had grave doubts.

As Pete walked in the moonlight pondering all this he knew plenty of other people owned 9MM automatic pistols. The trick was to find the gun which fired the bullet that killed Jessie Smith. My God, he thought! What if the joker who stole my pistol shot the boy? No matter, he thought. He had reported the pistol stolen months earlier. That didn't seem to carry much weight with the G.B.I. however. Pete felt that sooner or later something would turn up to point to the real killer.

As he trudged on through the night he kept a sharp lookout for any vehicle that might be traveling the road. He could see and hear a vehicle approaching from a long way at night. This gave him plenty of time to step off the road into the woods and not be seen.

Once he reached Moccasin Gap where Hannahatchee Creek flowed through a break in the hills there were a few houses scattered along the road. At this point he had some barking dogs to contend with. He had a strong stick that could deal with the dogs if he had to, but he didn't meet any dangerous dogs, just curious ones.

From Moccasin Gap he followed a county dirt road to the east. There were no houses on this road. As he gained altitude he could see the 1,700 foot T.V. tower at Cusseta with its red, blinking lights. Some of the parachute training tower at Ft. Benning came into view also. After a mile or so on the dirt road he turned into the woods to find the canyon and hide the rope. He found the canyon rim, but in the dark he couldn't locate a good hiding place for the rope. He decided to rest until daybreak, then hide the rope and proceed on to the cave. The route to the cave was entirely through the woods now so it wasn't as important to travel in the dark.

Pete stretched out on the pine straw under a stand of longleaf pines. Drawing his poncho about him he slept several hours until dawn. When he woke he ate some army C-rations then looked for a place to hide the rope close to the canyon rim. He decided on a hole in the ground where a stump had rotted. The sunken spot remained where a tree stump had rotted long ago. The hole left by the rotting stump had mostly filled with pine straw and debris. Pete cleaned out the hole, stuffed the rope in its plastic bag into the hole, and replaced the straw which covered the bag. Over the straw he placed a rock.

Stump holes were a common occurrence in the woods. Created when the stump of a tree either burned or rotted away, they were a hazard to man and beast. Many a broken or strained leg were caused by stump holes.

Pete pressed on toward the cave, confident that he could find the rope if the need arose. After crossing a mile wide plateau that was all in forest now, but had been in row crops for many years in the past, he descended into a creek bottom that was full of beaver dams. The creek bottom was about three miles long, and for its entire length, where each pond ended there was another dam which backed up more water. Pete crossed the bottom on a dam perhaps 100 yards long. He kept a sharp lookout for cottonmouth moccasins.

He knew of a man who had been bitten by a cottonmouth in this very same bottom several years before. The man lived in Albany. He traveled the highway from Albany to Columbus once a week. Every time he passed through the rugged terrain of northern Stewart County he would look across the hills and valleys about four miles to the west at a Forestry Commission fire lookout tower. He always wondered what the land looked like between the highway and the tower. One day in July he decided to find out. He wore his blue jeans and boots, parked his car, and headed for the lookout tower.

The land was rougher than he had ever imagined. He climbed in and out of canyons, and over steep ridges, but his biggest surprise was the valley he had to cross which was choked with beaver ponds. He crossed the valley on a beaver dam, and finally made it to the lookout tower located on a county dirt road. By now it was about noon. The temperature was in the 90's with lots of humidity. He was sweating profusely. He climbed the unmanned tower and could see his car parked on the shoulder of the highway four miles to the east. He enjoyed a little breeze on the tower and drank some water from his canteen. As he looked across the miles, he dreaded the trip back and wondered why he had chosen this hike in July instead of winter. Pete had wondered the same thing when the man related the story to him.

After a brief rest the man headed back toward his car. An hour later he came to the beaver ponds again. By now the temperature was in the high 90's. He was not wearing snake boots or snake chaps. As he reached the east bank of the beaver pond a cottonmouth moccasin struck him on the leg then slithered into the water. By the time the man made it to his car his leg was terribly swollen and turning blue. He was vomiting and dizzy, but drove his car about three miles to Richland and the emergency room of a hospital. He finally recovered, but he could easily have died.

Pete couldn't help but think about this incident as he crossed the beaver pond and headed to the cave. When he reached the cave he very thoroughly checked it for snakes. The cave would have made an ideal place for snakes to den up for the winter.

Once the roasted corn and jerky was safely stashed in metal storage cans he contemplated the trip back to the hill in the beaver ponds. He knew that he must stay away from areas that allowed public hunting until after deer season. He could return to the cave after Christmas when deer season was over. He also knew that he must be very careful in the reserve that was closed to public hunting. In short, he must be very careful wherever he was. If recognized now, he could be arrested for jumping bail as well as having to stand trial for murder. If only he could produce the murder weapon!

He decided to ride the motorcycle back to the beaver ponds. It would only take about thirty minutes on the motorcycle, and he could hide the motorcycle in the kudzu where he snared the deer. He decided to try the ride late at night when there was less chance of being seen. Pete carefully exited the cave and continued the two miles east to the kudzu patch beside the highway where the motorcycle was hidden. By then it was getting late in the day. He found the motorcycle where he had hidden it earlier. He kicked the starter a few times to make sure it would crank then ate some jerky and roasted corn and napped under his poncho until about three A.M.

At that time of morning there was hardly any traffic on the highway. Pete tied his pack on the luggage rack, rolled the motorcycle out of the kudzu, kicked the starter, and was off. A quick two miles north on the highway, brought him to the county dirt road to the west. As he motored through the night he passed by a hunting camp where he and friends and relatives had spent a week deer hunting every year in November as well as many weekends. He recognized his cousin's pickup parked at the camp. They had no doubt been there making preparations for the coming deer season. How he would have liked to see these people! But it was not to be. Pete was afraid that no matter how much a person wanted to keep a secret, he would probably let it slip somehow. He continued on through the night and had the motorcycle hidden well before daylight.

Jeff Callahan had signed his land into the wildlife preserve system along with Ft. Benning in order to reestablish deer into the area. In return, the government promised to patrol the area and strictly enforce the no hunting statutes.

Several years later Jeff entered into a 60 year lease on the land to Great Southern Paper Co. Great Southern managed the timberland as part of their Canyonlands Forest. Pete Lancaster had come to know Joe Schodski very well during the two years he had been there. They had become good friends. Even though the land was leased, Jeff was still trying to run things. Jeff was always telling Pete how the timber should be managed, and he was telling Joe how he should manage the wildlife.

Joe was very concerned when Pete was accused of shooting Jessie Smith. He had kept quiet about the fact that he was in the area with Jeff on the night of the shooting. He really didn't know any details. All he knew was that he had heard some shots. He had kept very quiet about his activities on that night all during the investigation. Jeff had told him that he had heard some shots, so he knew Jeff couldn't add anything to the investigation either. Joe wasn't particularly proud of the fact that he was out riding around with Jeff Callahan anyway.

During the investigation by the G.B.I. and the local sheriff's department it was established that Jessie Smith was killed by one round fired from a nine millimeter pistol. The investigators had the bullet. They just needed the murder weapon so they could fire a test round and compare the minute markings that the grooves in the pistol barrel left on the bullet. Since each individual gun has slight differences in the barrel, bullets traveling down that barrel will have distinctive markings on it that can be seen under high magnification.

When the G.B.I. asked Pete about his 9MM pistol he told them it had been stolen several months before, and he had reported it stolen to the sheriff of Stewart County where he lived. Pete told the investigators where he had done some target practice in the past. They dug some bullets out of a red clay bank and they did not match the bullet that killed Jessie Smith. This didn't stop the investigation however, because there was no proof which pistol had fired the bullets into the bank.

One day Joe saw Jeff Callahan and asked him if he had ever gone back and looked for his pistol.

Jeff said, "I went back and tried to walk where I was before, but never found it. I guess it is gone."

Joe said, "Well I could go help you look. I know you want to find Rommell's pistol."

"Nah, I don't think there's any use looking. They have been thinning the timber in there and got the place all torn up. I can't tell exactly where I was any way."

This conversation started Joe to thinking. My God, thought Joe! Jeff's pistol was a 9MM. He was in the general area where

Jessie Smith was killed. Could the Smith boy have been killed by Jeff? After all, wasn't he going over there to shoot some poachers? Maybe Jeff didn't want to find the pistol.

The next day Joe was in the Chattahoochee County sheriff's office. He and sheriff Walter Hooper were discussing the shooting of Jessie Smith and the disappearance of Pete Lancaster.

"Joe, I just don't believe Pete shot that boy", said Walter. "Somebody stole his pistol way back in the spring. The Stewart County sheriff made a report on it in May. He left it laying on the seat of his parked pickup for a while, and some folks were in the area grading roads. He was sure they stole it, but had no way of proving it."

"I know", said Joe, "he told me about it when it happened. He really hated to lose that gun. It had been given to him by a friend in Wisconsin. I don't believe he had bought another one either."

Walter said," You know, that 9MM is a real popular caliber. There are a lot of them around. A few months back this guy who has a mobile home over there near Jeff Callahan's lake had gone shopping with his wife. When they came home they noticed a bullet hole in the wall of their bedroom. The bedroom door was open and the bullet came down the hall, hit the wall in the kitchen, then landed in the kitchen floor. They found the bullet in the floor and called me. It was a 9MM. If they had been home someone might have been killed. They have the bullet in a little plastic bag. I filed a report on it. It seems like just an incident of a stray bullet."

Joe asked, "Do they have any idea who might have fired the gun?"

"Well," the sheriff said, "they claim that at times there are some wild parties down there around Jeff's lake, and they think that someone might have been shooting just for the hell of it without an adequate backstop. They just don't know."

"What's their name?" said Joe.

"Linda and Marvin Dupree", said Walter.

After leaving the sheriff's office Joe's mind was on the bullet the man in the mobile home had found. Was it possible that

Jeff or someone in his family had fired the stray bullet that hit the mobile home? And was it possible that it was fired from the pistol that Jeff claimed was Rommells? Could this also be the gun that killed Jessie Smith? He finally decided that this was a possibility worth looking into. But what could he do? He couldn't go to the G.B.I. with this theory with nothing to substantiate it. It would be political suicide to even suggest such a thing, since Jeff Callahan was a big time banker who had signed the land where Joe worked into the wildlife preserve. If only he had Jeff's gun! In the meantime he would have to keep these thoughts to himself.

Safely back on the hill in the swamp Pete rested the next day. He reset the fish basket and baked some potatoes in the ashes of his campfire. It was the last of October. The weather was getting colder, and the leaves were brilliant. Some were beginning to fall. Today was Wednesday. Deer season would open on the Georgia side of the river Saturday. The deer hunters would be pouring into the woods and fields on Friday. Pete knew he would have to drastically reduce his movement – especially the first weekend of deer season. He didn't want to just sit around and do nothing, so he decided to take the canoe and visit some of the farmland on the Alabama side of the river the first few days of deer season. Pete knew that the game wardens would be on the lookout for poachers on the Georgia side, and he would have to be extra cautious. The deer season didn't open until the last of November in Alabama.

Pete packed food, clothes, etc for a one week stay. He carried some warm clothes, poncho, army c-rations, some parched corn and smoked fish. He didn't know exactly where he was going or what conditions would be. He had a small A.M.-F.M. radio with weather channel. The morning temperature was predicted to be in the 30's with no rain for the foreseeable future. Late in the day he made his way to the river, recovered the canoe, and loaded his supplies.

He waited until dark and paddled out into the river. This time of year, people were rarely on the river after dark, especially in the middle of the week. He could hear motorboats for a long distance in the quiet of the night if any were on the river. He figured he could take cover and not be seen if he heard one. The air was crisp and cool as he paddled downstream.

After traveling about two miles downstream Pete entered a small stream emptying into the river from the west. He couldn't go far before the stream became too shallow for the canoe. He beached the canoe and made a rough camp to spend the night. He decided to stay close to the river on land owned by the Army Corps of Engineers. That way, if someone stumbled across his camp, he wouldn't be accused of trespassing on private property. In fact, he had decided to tell anyone who questioned him that he was making a trip all the way down the Chattahoochee from the north Georgia mountains to Apalachicola, Florida where the river runs into the Gulf of Mexico.

After spending a frosty night in the down sleeping bag without pitching a tent he built a small fire and cooked some breakfast. The leaves were brilliant and the sky was clear as he contemplated his next move. After breakfast he found a hiding place for the canoe where a ditch intersected the creek. After securing the canoe and most of his supplies he shouldered the pack and began to explore the immediate area in the adjacent river bottom.

The land was in a big horseshoe bend of the river. It was mostly planted pine about ten years old on land that was formerly row crop and pasture land. Pete knew from past experience that timberland in this age class was for the most part left alone. There was nothing to be done with it but leave it alone until it grew to a size that could be thinned for pulpwood or perhaps control burned. It could be thinned as early as twelve years on the rich, bottomland soil. At any rate it should be fairly safe from human activity. There was something like a thousand acres of planted pine in the big bend of the river. This was surrounded by hard-wood trees along the river and the streams on either side of the big river bend.

About one half mile back from the river, where the hills began to rise from the river plain was an abandoned settlement. Two old houses remained with their roofs falling in. An old concrete silo and a windmill tower still stood. Foundations of others houses remained where buildings had been torn down. An old log cabin with a leaky wood shingle roof still stood and back in the hardwoods was a small barn, overgrown with vines. It had a tin roof and still had loose hay on the floor and a few bales of hay inside. The building was very old, but still essentially sound. A big owl flew out of it when Pete approached. Pete hid a few C-rations from his pack under the hay. He thought he might make this a camp if the weather turned bad. He loaded his pack with pecans from some old trees he found in the old settlement.

He followed an old road that led out of the place to see where it went. After proceeding another one half mile to the west he came to a locked gate where the old road joined a county maintained dirt road. He retraced his steps back to the river. He found several persimmon trees along the way and managed to shake off quite a few to eat. The deer and other animals had cleaned up the ones that had fallen. The opossums and raccoons climb the trees to eat them.

Pete went fishing that afternoon. As he fished from the river bank he noticed the big C-124 cargo planes flying low and slow up the river. On the Alabama side of the river a little farther upstream was the paratrooper drop zone. Soldiers undergoing airborne training were dropped thirty to forty at a time from the cargo planes. From a higher elevation up on the hills one could see the parachutes floating down.

The weather was crisp and clear with little wind. It was a beautiful fall day. Occasionally an outboard motor powered bass boat would go up or down the river. Pete would move back into the bushes and remain out of sight until the boat passed. Fishing from the bank he caught several bass and some catfish.

He was walking back toward his camp with the fish when he saw something white about one hundred yards ahead. He thought it was a piece of Styrofoam that had broken loose from a dock and floated down and lodged during some high water. He had seen quite a few of these blocks along with plastic bottles and all kinds of floating debris that accumulated in certain spots when the river flooded. When he got within about fifty yards of the white object it sprang to its feet and ran. It was an albino deer- a very rare animal, and the only one that Pete had ever seen. Poor thing, thought Pete. It had a hard time remaining hidden.

The next day Pete stayed around camp and baked his fish on a board staked in front of a small campfire. After completing this task he decided to separate some of his supplies and store them in two different locations in case someone should find them, he wouldn't lose everything. He did this by moving some supplies back into the young planted pines. There he pitched his tent among the thick pines and undergrowth.

The next day was opening day of deer season across the river in Georgia. Sporadic gunfire could be heard up and down the river all day on the Georgia side. There were very few fishing boats on the river. Pete surmised that many of the people who normally would have been fishing were deer hunting. The weekend passed with crystal clear days and cold nights. From the sporadic gunfire that could be heard, especially in the morning and late afternoon the hunters must be enjoying a successful weekend of deer hunting.

On Monday the weather warmed up and the wind came from the south – off the Gulf of Mexico. The wind was mild at first. On Tuesday the wind from the gulf became stronger. It became cloudy, and there was the definite feel of moisture in the air. An occasional shot could be heard from across the river, but evidently the hunting had tapered off. Pete knew from experience that there would never be as much activity in the woods as opening weekend.

On Wednesday the wind switched to the northeast and the rain began. It started as light sprinkles but steadily increased as the wind became stronger and the temperature dropped. Pete decided to move to the old barn he had found earlier. He left the tent but took his sleeping bag and some food and headed for the barn wearing his poncho. The big owl flew out through a hole in the wall as he entered the barn.

The rain beat a steady rap on the tin roof of the barn and the wind moaned through the trees. It was good to have a dry place out of the elements, but it was cold with no hope for a fire for warmth. All Pete could do was sit there and think about his alternatives. He knew that if he was caught he would go to jail. If he was falsely convicted of murder he could be executed. He had some money. He had grown a beard. He could get to Columbus, buy a bus ticket, leave this part of the country and possibly start a new life. No one would be looking for him, because they thought he was dead. This was a plan that would probably succeed, but it offered no chance of proving his innocence. He really thought that some evidence would turn up to prove his innocence. He thought that if he could hold on something would turn up. In the meantime he had to survive.

Pete slipped into his sleeping bag and listened to the radio with headphones while the rain drummed on the old metal roof, and the northeast wind moaned through the trees outside. As he half dozed he heard a different noise outside. He turned off the radio and listened. Over the noise of the rain on the roof he heard the unmistakable throb of a diesel engine. He got up and looked through a crack in the old clapboard siding. A diesel powered, white, pickup truck with a cover over the pickup bed had come down the road into the old settlement. It stopped about fifty yards from the barn. That was as close as they could drive because small trees and brush had grown up around the barn in the years since the place was abandoned. Pete wondered what they were doing there on a day like this. He started to hide his things under the hay, slip out of the barn, and leave through the woods behind the barn. He decided that they might possibly see him, so he waited and watched with his heart in his throat

To his consternation two men got out of the truck with raincoats on and started toward the barn. Pete grabbed his belongings and ran up the stairs into the barn loft. There were some old hay bales up there also. He crouched behind the hay and remained quiet. He could hear the men talking as they came into the barn below, but couldn't understand what they were saying. They soon left. When he heard the door shut down below he eased up to a crack and observed the men going to the truck. Each carried one of the hay bales. They placed the bales in the covered truck bed, cranked the truck and left.

Pete wondered why men needed old hay so badly they would come to this remote location over terrible roads in this kind of weather. And then they only got two bales. After he was satisfied they had left the area he came back downstairs and took a close look at the hay bales. He cut the twine binding one bale and opened it up. In the center of the bale was a hollowed out area containing plastic bags of a white powder. There were five bags containing about two pounds each. My God, thought Pete! This stuff must be cocaine! What a hiding place this was. He thought he had a very secure, dry, hiding place for himself. Instead, he had deposited himself right in the middle of someone's drug operation. He decided to leave immediately. The people probably wouldn't come back today, but who knew.

He packed his belongings, including the ten pounds of cocaine, put on his poncho and left the protection of the old barn. He took the opened hay bale and deposited it in the woods behind the barn, then headed back to the tent in the planted pines. The last thing he needed was to get caught with cocaine, but in a real pinch it could come in very handy. When he reached the tent he put the cocaine in a waterproof ammo box, dug a hole, and buried it beside a big, dead oak tree.

The rain stopped early the next day. Pete decided to return to the Georgia side of the river. He rounded up his supplies, retrieved the canoe, and that night made his way upriver to the stream from the beaver ponds. It was still cloudy and very dark, but he made the trip by sparingly using a flashlight. The stream was running full because of the recent rain. Pete pulled the canoe up to its hiding place at the ditch, unloaded it, and made a cold camp for the rest of the night.

Next morning he hid the canoe and made his way through the beaver pond to the hill. The weather was clearing and turning colder. The planes were dropping paratroopers again, and the north wind was bringing sounds of automatic weapons and the dull thud of mortars firing on the Ft. Benning training grounds to the north.

Pete was beginning to need a few items that he knew he must buy. He knew he couldn't walk into a store in the small towns where he was so well known. Columbus was the logical place to buy the items. He could also spend a little time there until the hunter's numbers diminished. But how could he get there? He could paddle the canoe upriver, but decided a fifteen mile river trip through Ft. Benning would attract too much attention. He could ride the motorcycle into Columbus, but where would he leave it if he stayed in a motel? He couldn't hide it in Columbus, and if a cop should run a tag check that turned up his name it could cause trouble. He thought about riding it to the outskirts of Cusseta, hiding it, and catching the bus to Columbus. However with the number of people in the woods now , someone might see him hide the motorcycle. He decided to pack a bag and walk to the combination service station and bus stop at Cusseta and catch the Greyhound bus to Columbus. He waited another day and started the following night.

It was about ten miles to Cusseta. Pete figured he could make it in three hours easily. He knew there was a bus from Florida going north shortly after daybreak. He hit the road with clean clothes and a pack about 3:00 A.M.

Norma and Larry got a call from Marvin Johnson, the district forester with Great Southern Paper Co. The man had been Pete Lancaster's boss at the main office at Cedar Springs, Georgia. Mr. Johnson explained that something had to be done with the clothes and furnishings in the house that Pete had occupied at the forest headquarters in Lumpkin. Norma also was the beneficiary on Pete's company life insurance policy.

"Mrs. Edenview, it's been two months now since Pete disappeared," explained Mr. Johnson. "We have to do something with all of Pete's things. We are going to have to replace Pete and move someone else into his house."

"Well you know we can't settle his estate until he has been missing for a year," said Norma. "But I can understand your need for the house. We will just have to come down and move the stuff into storage."

Norma and Larry had visited Pete many times during the past two years since his graduation from forestry school and employment by Great Southern Paper Co. Larry liked to hunt with Pete, and Norma enjoyed hiking in the Little Grand Canyon Park as well as visiting the wives of Pete's friends in the area. They decided to take some vacation time, drive to Lumpkin in Pete's truck, and clean out the company house where Pete had lived. They had already brought his guns and some other personal items to their home in Atlanta for safe keeping. Their intent this trip was to completely clean out the house. They would bring all his clothes and other personal items to their home and store the furniture until they could legally settle his estate. Without the knowledge of his friends and relatives, Pete had purchased and concealed the motorcycle and canoe prior to his disappearance on the river.

When Norma and Larry reached Lumpkin they contacted Mr. Marvin Johnson at the forest headquarters then started packing Pete's clothes and personal items in boxes. They rented a storage bin in town and used Pete's pickup to haul the furniture to the storage bin. They were eating lunch at the "Back of the Moon Restaurant" in town and saw several people they had met in the past. They were all questioning them about the whereabouts of Pete, and wondering if any new information had turned up.

Suddenly Joe Schodski, the game warden, approached their table.

"Well hello there Norma and Larry," said Joe . "I saw Pete's truck outside and thought maybe he had found his way back to Lumpkin."

"No", said Larry, "We are just moving his stuff into storage until we can settle his estate. Come on, have a seat and eat lunch with us."

Joe sat down and immediately began to ask the same questions about Pete that the other friends and neighbors had been asking. Of course there was nothing new to tell anyone.

Norma said, "Joe, I know your feelings about this case are the same as ours. We just do not believe that Pete shot that boy.

47

What makes this whole thing so hard is that Pete disappeared under these circumstances – with a murder charge against him. I am convinced that he died on the Ocmulgee River, and will never have a chance to prove his innocence."

As they sat there eating and discussing the circumstances of the case for the umpteenth time Joe felt more and more guilt and remorse for not revealing his suspicions about Jeff Callahan. Finally he decided, what the hell, I am going to put the ball in Larry and Norma's court and let them run with it.

"Norma," said Joe, "I am going to tell you something that could result in a new light being thrown on this case, but I don't want you to let anyone know how you found it out."

Norma said, "Joe you know I will keep it confidential if it is important to you."

"Well at this time it is very important," said Joe, "however if this leads anywhere I may be able to furnish some more information. I want you to go to the G.B.I. office when you get back to Atlanta. Talk to the agents who investigated this case, and tell them that a couple who live in a mobile home near Cusseta have a 9M.M. pistol bullet that was fired into their home back in the summer. Tell them you have reason to believe that it may have the same markings as the bullet that killed Jessie Smith. The people are Linda and Marvin Dupree, and they live on county road No. nine out by the railroad siding where they load pulpwood. Walter Hooper, the sheriff up there, has some information on it. In fact he filed a report when it happened. The G.B.I. is at a standstill on this case. They would welcome any kind of information."

"Can the G.B.I. confiscate the bullet," said Norma?

"I doubt it," said Joe, "not without some evidence to tie it to some crime; but I expect the people will be more than happy to have the bullet checked out."

Norma said, "Joe, what makes you think this bullet may have come from the same gun that killed Jessie Smith, and why didn't you tell the G.B.I. about this when they were here investigating?"

"Well, I didn't know about this bullet until a few days ago," said Joe, "and I can reveal more about my suspicions after the bullet is checked out, but until it is checked out please keep my name out of this."

"O.K., when we get back to Atlanta we will see what we can do."

It took most of two days for Norma and Larry to get Pete's things packed up and in storage. They moved everything out of the house, picked up a few personal items from the office, and told Mr. Johnson at the Canyonlands Forest headquarters they were leaving for Atlanta. "Mr. Johnson," said Norma, "next fall when Pete has been missing for a year we will get the necessary documents from the probate judge and come to settle Pete's estate."

"Well Norma, I can't tell you how sorry I am about having to replace Pete, but our work must go on. I don't have any hope of replacing Pete with someone as good."

Norma and Larry said they would stay in touch and headed back to Atlanta with Pete's clothes and personal items. On the trip back, Norma and Larry were discussing the latest turn of events. Norma asked Larry, "What do you think of this situation about the bullet in the house trailer?"

Larry responded, "I don't know what to think, but obviously Joe attaches a lot of importance to it. I don't know what connection there could possibly be, but we will talk to the G.B.I.

CHAPTER VI

The northbound Greyhound bus pulled into the station in downtown Columbus at about 8:30 A.M. Pete made his way north, with his backpack, a few blocks and checked into a hotel that offered cheap weekly rates. It was used by a lot of construction workers, etc. He paid a week in advance with cash under the name of Ruben Ware from Atlanta, Ga. He ate a good breakfast in the hotel cafeteria – the first restaurant food in a long time. He was very tired from the long hike and being up all night. After breakfast he lay on the bed to take a nap, but slept all day.

Pete was making this trip primarily to kill time. He thought that after another week of deer season the number of hunters would diminish, and the woods would be safer for him. He killed time by going to the movies, visiting the library and museums. He knew that he might run into someone whom he would know, but felt sure that his appearance had changed so much that he wouldn't be recognized. He now had a full beard. He wore a cap and sunglasses any time he was outside.

He liked to walk on the river walk. It was a park that extended several miles along the river, down to Ft. Benning. There were hiking trails, picnic areas, trees and flowers. It was a good place to sit and read or walk and let the time pass. One day he walked past Jeff Callahan's office on First Avenue; a street that paralleled the river. He noticed a white pickup, with a cover on the back, parked in Jeff's parking lot. My gosh, thought Pete, that looks like the truck I saw at the barn that rainy day! He bought a Columbus paper from a rack on the street then took a seat on a park bench across the street from Jeff's office. After a while two men came out of Jeff's office, got in the pickup, and drove away. Pete saw enough to realize that it was the same two men he had seen getting the hay bales from the barn that rainy day. The truck had an Alabama license plate, and Pete wrote down the number.

Pete had heard that Jeff owned some land across the river in Alabama. He didn't know where the land was or how much he

50

owned. Could it be possible that these men were employed by Jeff and dealing in drugs without his knowledge? Or another possibility was that Jeff was involved directly. As Pete thought over the whole situation he became seriously determined to find out more.

Across the river from Columbus, Ga. was Phenix City, Alabama. It was the county seat of Russell County which encompassed the land where Pete had taken refuge from the rain in the old barn. Pete hiked on up First Avenue a few blocks to the Fourteenth Street bridge which connected Columbus with Phenix City. As soon as he crossed the river the courthouse was on the left. He entered the courthouse and went to the tax appraiser's office. Since the tax records are open to the public, he had no trouble locating the parcel on a map in the big river bend where the old barn was located. After getting the map and parcel number he then went to the tax digest to see who owned that parcel of land. Sure enough, it was owned by Jeff Callahan and there were 1,280 acres in the parcel. Well, he thought, this is very interesting, but it doesn't prove anything except who owns the land.

One night at the movie theatre he realized that a young couple from Lumpkin that he knew very well was in line behind him. He would have liked very much to talk to them, but knew that he dare not. They didn't recognize him so that made him feel that his disguise was working.

Later that night, back at the hotel, Pete was taking stock of his assets. He still had some cash, but it wasn't going to last forever. He had hidden some cash at each of his camps. Some was at the cave, and some was on the hill in the beaver ponds. He hadn't been out of school and working long enough to accumulate a lot of savings, although he did have some. He had withdrawn enough to buy the motorcycle and canoe. He hid them after he conceived the plan to fake his death. He had bought a good many supplies and hidden about two thousand dollars. He didn't want to close his bank account completely. That would look suspicious. What he didn't know was, how long must he keep hiding before some evidence turned up that would pinpoint the real killer?

He thought of all kinds of possibilities like leaving this part of the country, taking on a new identity, etc. He thought he could possibly pull it off, but he didn't want to remain a fugitive forever. He wanted to pick up a lead to the real killer somehow, and he knew he had to stay in the area to do it. He thought about the ten pounds of cocaine he had hidden and wondered what its value was. One thing was for certain, circumstances would have to be extreme indeed before he touched the cocaine. He thought he could trap a few furbearing animals and sell the fur for some extra money. This was something he thought he could do fairly easily while hiding out. He decided to open a checking account in his name at a Columbus bank so he could deposit a check for the fur there. When he walked into the bank to open an account he found fifty dollars laying on the steps. He thought about going in and asking if anyone had lost fifty dollars. Then he thought that would only call attention to himself, and besides too many people might try to claim it.

During the next few days Pete did a little shopping for the items he needed, such as new batteries for his radio, a small roll of wire for trapping, some whiskey, cheese, some pain killing medication and a few canned goods. At the end of the week he caught the southbound bus to Cusseta at night, got off the bus and started the hike back to his camp.

A cold wind was blowing from the north as he walked south down U.S. Hwy. 27. There were several houses and a mobile home park along this portion of the route. As Pete walked past one house a big, black dog barked ferociously and followed him down the road barking. Pete drew his pistol, but knew he must only fire as a last resort. The dog finally quit barking and went back to the house. Pete decided that if he walked this route again he would have something other than a pistol to handle bad dogs.

There were no houses on the last seven miles of the highway back to the river. He stepped off the road twice when vehicles passed. One vehicle was a game warden's truck, and Pete was pretty sure it was Joe Schodski. He arrived back at the hill in the beaver ponds late at night with a cold north wind blowing.

It was the middle of November. There was frost in the bottomland along the river every night. Some mornings there was thin ice in the shallow areas of the beaver ponds. Fur on the furbearing animals was definitely prime now.

Pete made plans to start trapping. He knew he had to be very careful where he set traps. Trapping as well as hunting was forbidden on the refuge, and if a game warden were to see one of his traps or trapped animals, he might wait in hiding to catch the trapper. Rather than cover a large area which would require a lot of walking or canoeing and expose himself to more risk of being caught, or rather discovered, he decided to intensively trap small areas then move to another spot. Running a trap line was difficult enough under the best of circumstances. It was hard to hide traps from animals being trapped, but it was doubly hard to hide them from man and animals.

Since deer season was still in progress he decided to confine the trapping to areas that were not open to public hunting such as the game refuge, Ft. Benning , and the strip of land along the river controlled by the Army Corps of Engineers. The Corps of Engineers issued permits for bow hunting only – no firearms on the Corps land along the river. The general public hunted on Corps land as opposed to timber company and private land, a lot of which was leased to hunting clubs. His presence on the Corps land would not arouse suspicion like it would on the private land.

The first traps were set in beaver ponds about one half mile from the complex of ponds where Pete was hiding. He used a combination of killer Connibear traps and steel traps along with deadfalls and snares. The traps were set for beaver, muskrat, otter and mink traveling up and down the streams. Raccoons, foxes, and other land animals were caught mostly in the sets made where the animals crossed the ponds on the beaver dams. Some sets were made underwater where the trapped animal quickly drowned. Other sets were made above the water line with the trap attached, by a one way slider, to a wire leading into deep water. The snares and deadfalls had no doubt been in use for thousands of years as a means of capturing animals.

The deadfall was made by placing one log on the ground and another over it supported by a wooden trigger. The system of logs was held together by stakes driven into the ground on each side of the logs. It could be built to accommodate any size animal.

Pete carried his hip boots and wore them when he reached the beaver ponds. The animals he caught were skinned and the excess fat and flesh scraped from the hides in the area where they were caught. The hides were then carried back to camp and dried on frames made from hickory saplings. The big beavers would weigh thirty to forty pounds and were very difficult to skin. He would carry them out of the pond and into thick brush to skin them. He knew he couldn't watch for other people who may be in the area and concentrate on skinning at the same time.

One day while carrying a beaver to the edge of a pond to be skinned he suddenly stepped into a deep hole in the pond. He went in up to his shoulders. He dropped the beaver and grabbed a small sapling. That is the only thing that kept him from going completely under. The hip boots filled with water and made it very difficult for him to pull himself out of the hole. When he did get out he struggled to dry land, removed the boots and wet clothes, and built a small fire with waterproof matches from his pack. He had extra underwear and socks in a waterproof bag for just such an emergency. He wrung his clothes out and dried them a while by the fire. He put on the dry underwear and socks and wrapped up in his poncho while the clothes dried. After the clothes partially dried he put out the fire, got dressed, and returned to the pond to look for the beaver he had dropped. It wasn't to be found. It had sunk. Two days later he found it floating and skinned it.

After about ten days of trapping in that location he decided to move across the line on to Ft. Benning. There didn't seem to be a lot of military activity in that area now, and there were beaver ponds galore that were rich with fur.

From time to time Pete would dig up some of the food he had stored in the holes in the ground of his camp on the hill. One day while digging he uncovered an Indian bowl. A little more digging produced a soapstone pipe and a tomahawk. My gosh, thought Pete, this hill I am camped on must be an Indian mound! He hadn't given any thought to why a small hill suddenly popped up in the middle of flat bottomland. No telling what could be found by a complete excavation of the mound, but Pete didn't have the facilities or the inclination for that much digging. He had friends who were historians and archeologists. They would certainly be interested in this mound. This made Pete even more anxious for an end to his seclusion so he could proceed with this and other projects.

A few miles down the river at Rood Creek was a whole complex of Indian mounds. About fifty miles farther down river near Blakely, Georgia were the Kolomoki mounds. Some of these had been excavated, and their contents were on display in a museum there. From what Pete had heard about the mounds, the native population that occupied them left the area about 1200 A.D. The Indian tribes that occupied the land when Europeans settled here had no knowledge of the mound builders.

The military base, Ft. Benning, covered 182,000 acres – one of the largest military bases in the nation. The housing and training facilities on the base were concentrated on the north end of the base, closer to Columbus. The south end wasn't used nearly as much. It was mostly vast, unbroken tracts of timberland.

CHAPTER VII

Back in Atlanta Larry and Norma visited the G.B.I. office one Friday afternoon. They stated their business and proclaimed that they had some information that could possibly shed new light on the murder of Jessie Smith. They were directed to the two agents who had been assigned the case when sheriff Walter Hooper requested help. The agents were out of the office, but Larry and Norma were informed that the agents would be in Monday morning. Their names were James McIntire and Douglas Slagle.

Monday morning found Larry and Norma back at the G.B.I. office, and meeting with McIntire and Slagle. Larry and Norma told the agents about their recent trip to Lumpkin .

In addressing the agents Larry said, "We have run across some information that might shed some new light on who shot the judge's boy. While we were at Lumpkin we were approached by someone who we are not at liberty to name at this time. However our source has assured us that if this evidence checks out as they think it will, then they will tell us what the connection is. It seems that a 9M.M. pistol bullet was fired into someone's mobile home in Chattahoochee County last summer. The people who live in the home still have the bullet. Mr. Hooper, the Chattahoochee County Sheriff, made a report on the incident, but he doesn't have any knowledge of the facts that might tie this bullet to the gun that killed Jessie Smith. We think Linda and Marvin Dupree will be glad to let you have the bullet for testing to see if it matches the bullet that killed Jessie Smith. The person who gave us this information seems to think that it is a strong possibility."

Norma said, "What do you think? Do you believe it is worth a try?"

Doug Slagle responded with, "Yeah, sure it's worth a try. Do you think this could lead us to the gun that fired the bullet?"

Norma said, "Well we certainly hope so, but at this time we can't be certain."

The agents, McIntire and Slagle assured Norma and Larry that they would try to get the bullet and test it.

Pete packed a light tent, sleeping bag, food, and extra clothes on a pack frame. He then hiked a couple of miles north, parallel to the river, and into the southern edge of Ft. Benning. He kept away from roads and stayed strictly in the woods. He was wearing camouflage clothes, His mission now was to find a good trapping area and a very secure place to set up camp close to the trap line.

He came upon a small stream entering the river with a series of beaver dams on it. It was much like the stream where he had been hiding except that the stream was smaller. On a hill nearby was a stand of young pines that was very thick. The trees were 15 – 20 feet tall and perhaps ten years old. He cleared a small area with his machete and pitched the tent. The dense vegetation in the young pine stand would hide his camp and cook fires very well. Anyone traveling through the woods on foot would certainly avoid such a thick, brushy area. It was probably as secure as any place that could be found. The thick brush kept the cold, north wind from penetrating the camp. He had to be careful about establishing a trail into the camp. This could be accomplished very easily by not coming and going by the same route repeatedly.

Late that afternoon Pete set some wire snares on the beaver dams, then ate some jerky and crawled in his sleeping bag. Next morning he returned to his camp downstream to bring back steel traps, hip boots, the fish trap and some more food including some peanuts and roast corn. Arriving back at the new camp he began to seriously set traps for furbearers.

The fish trap was a steady producer of bream and catfish. After cleaning, these were nailed to a strip of green wood and roasted by the fire. The fish heads made excellent bait for otter, raccoon, fox, and bobcat sets. Sometimes a fresh killed raccoon or beaver would be skinned, gutted, placed in a damp burlap bag and baked in a hole in the ground lined with coals from the fire. It would take about twelve hours to thoroughly cook the animal using this method. Hickory nuts were gathered and shelled. Briar roots were gathered, pounded to a pulp, and baked over coals to make a bread substitute.

As the days wore on the fur began to accumulate. There was beaver, stretched on green hickory poles, bent to form a circle, with the green hides laced to the frame with a big needle and nylon line. Otter, muskrat, and raccoon were dried with the skin side out and a green hickory stick bent to form a U and inserted inside the green hide which had been peeled off like a sock.

The accumulation of these furs began to be a problem. They needed to be kept out of the weather in order to dry properly. Pete had kept them under a tarp next to the tent, but the place had become crowded. They needed about two more weeks of drying time.

Pete remembered an old farm building on the land he had previously managed. This was on the wildlife refuge down south of Ft. Benning. In fact it was close to the area where Jessie Smith was killed. Pete thought this would be a good place to stash the fur while it completed the drying process. It was about four miles south of his present location. Over to the east about one half mile was a road that ran from the main part of Ft. Benning in the north to a mortar firing range farther south. Occasionally Pete would see army buses and trucks on this road. After leaving the Ft. Benning property the road continued on to the abandoned farm where the old log house was located. Evidently this had been a county road long before Ft. Benning was established.

Pete lashed the fur, complete with hickory stretchers to a pack frame, shouldered the pack , and made his way east. When he hit the road going to the mortar range he waited a while to make sure there was no activity on the road. Everything seemed quiet so he started hiking south on the road. After going about a mile the road forked with one road leading off farther east toward the mortar firing range. At the intersection there was a stack of ten cases of M.R.E.'s (meals ready to eat). There were also ammo boxes full of linked, blank machine gun ammunition. Obviously these supplies had been left for someone to pick up, and it would probably be soon. Pete faded into the wood and shed his pack frame. He came back and hurriedly grabbed three cases of the M.R.E.'s and ran into the woods with them. He placed two boxes behind a big pine tree and covered them with straw. He then hiked south in the woods staying parallel to the road with the fur on his back and one case of M.R.E.'s under his arm. A case of M.R.E.'s had enough dried food for twelve meals and weighed about fifteen pounds. He stayed off the road until he left Ft. Benning.

Upon arriving at the old, log house he had initially thought he would hide the fur as best he could among some old, broken, mule-drawn, farm equipment, and rolls of rusty barbed wire. In looking for the best place to hide the fur he noticed the hole providing access to the attic. He climbed up and looked around. This, he decided, would provide a better hiding place, at least from the casual observer. He spaced the fur around in the attic then came down and opened some M.R.E.'s. He had heard soldiers complain about the quality of food in these field rations, but compared to what he had been eating it was great. After eating, Pete stashed the remaining M.R.E.'s in the house and headed back up the road. When he reached the place where he had stashed the other two cases of M.R.E.'s he tied them to his pack frame. He noticed that the stacked rations and ammo was gone. Someone had picked them up.

It was the middle of December. About three weeks was left in the deer season. After Pete got back to his camp in the thick, young, pines he decided to move his camp and trap line again. It was a good time to move since he had just hidden the fur. The area he had been trapping was producing a lot less fur, so it was time for a change. Pete figured that a new territory would last until deer season was over. After that, he could extend his operating area without fear of discovery by hunters, and trap on timber company land to the south.

He decided to move about a mile farther north and closer to the river. In fact, he decided he would trap directly on the river, and when he was ready to move back to the hill in the beaver ponds, three miles to the south, he could use the canoe. The area he chose for a camp was another dense, young, stand of pines on a hill beside the river. He pitched the tent, as before, among the thick pines.

Down the hill from this camp was a very small stream that ran through a beautiful hardwood cove into the river. The bowl shaped cove of ten to twelve acres, just off the river, contained one of the few areas of old growth timber Pete had ever seen in this part of the country. The timber was mostly oak with a scattering of beech, hickory, yellow poplar, and a few old pines. The trees were obviously up to two hundred years old. Over a hill to the south was a stand of pine approximately one hundred years old. It was growing in the rich, river bottom, soil. The trees averaged about 120 feet tall and timber volume was approximately 50,000 board feet per acre. They would make veneer and high quality saw timber. At current prices the pines were worth approximately $20,000 per acre. Pete couldn't help but wonder how the hardwood cove had escaped being cleared for agriculture when the country was settled, but obviously it had escaped the axe and plow. The pine stand had most likely seeded in on an old field abandoned shortly after the civil war.

Traps and snares were set along the river and along the small streams emptying into the river. This kind of forest required a little different trapping technique. There were a lot of den trees; old hollow trees that various animals made home. The most valuable fur was bobcat, but they were never very plentiful. The next most valuable was otter. They lived primarily on fish and had trails in and out of the river, especially where streams intersected the river. Fish scales, evidence of their diet, were concentrated on the river bank in places where the otter chose to come out and eat. Carefully laid steel traps with a drowning wire attached were very productive at these sites.

While attending traps along the river Pete was careful to remain unobserved. He was trapping on an army post, but river traffic up and down the river by sport fishermen as well as some army watercraft was common. Across the river on the Alabama side was the drop zone where C-17 aircraft dropped paratroopers during training exercises. Each plane dropped about forty paratroopers.

While Pete was busy trapping and trying to stay hidden he was concerned that he was making no progress in finding Jessie Smith's real killer. He considered contacting his sister in Atlanta, but decided not to at this time. For some reason, he felt that if he stayed in the area he would sooner or later find some evidence that would free him. In the meantime, he trapped, worked to find enough food, and worked at staying hidden. He listened to the news from a Columbus radio station every night. The Christmas holidays were approaching. The weather was getting real nasty with a lot of rain and cold.

Shortly after Norma and Larry visited the G.B.I. in Atlanta the agents, James McIntire and Douglas Slagle made a trip down to Cusseta. They went by to see the Sheriff, Walter Hooper. "What do you know about a bullet being fired into a mobile home owned by Linda and Marvin Dupree," Slagle asked Hooper?

"Well, I know they found holes in the walls and a bullet in the floor when they came home from shopping one day. I made a report on it back last summer sometime. Best I could figure, it was just a stray bullet. Why are you guys concerned about that bullet?"

"We can't tell you at this point where we got the information, but someone who heard about it thinks there is a good chance it matches the bullet that killed Jessie Smith."

"Well why in the world would they think that? What are they going on, Hooper said?"

"We don't know enough of the background at this point. We just want to pick up the bullet and test it. If it matches the bullet that killed Jessie Smith we have been assured that some more information will be forthcoming."

Walter said, "Well I'll go out there with you and we'll see if they will let us have the bullet."

When they reached the mobile home Mrs. Linda Dupree was home. Mr. Hooper introduced the two G.B.I. agents and explained their mission. Mrs. Dupree brought out the bullet which had been kept in a plastic bag. She also pointed out the bullet holes in the mobile home, and noted that the entrance hole was on the end of the home facing property owned by Jeff Callahan.

Mr. Callahan lived in Columbus, but he owned about 200 acres on the edge of Cusseta. This property had a nice, man-made lake with a pavilion on the shoreline where he entertained guests occasionally.

Mrs. Dupree said, "I think they have some pretty wild parties down there. I don't know if they have a firing range or not, but we hear shooting quite frequently. I know they have some dove hunts in the fall. Of course they are using shotguns on their dove hunts. There is a distinct difference in the sound of a shotgun and pistol anyway. This shot came through our wall in late summer before dove season opened. We weren't here when this shot was fired, but we saw it as soon as we came home."

Slagle asked Mrs. Dupree, "What makes you think the bullet came from Mr. Callahan's property?"

"I don't know that it did", responded Mrs. Dupree. "All I know is that I have heard firing in that direction many times before. I think there is a good chance the bullet came from there."

Sheriff Hooper said, "I went down to talk to them after the Duprees called, but there was no one there. I called Jeff later and told him what happened. He could offer no explanation."

The agents, McIntire and Slagle explained to Mrs. Dupree that they would like to test the bullet. "There is a possibility this would furnish information on some other cases we are investigating," explained Mr. McIntire.

"Sure, take it and test it", said Mrs. Dupree. "It's no good to us."

The sheriff and G.B.I. agents thanked Mrs. Dupree and left. When the agents returned to Atlanta, they took the bullet they had obtained from Mrs. Dupree along with the bullet retrieved from Jessie Smith's body to the laboratory. They explained that they wanted a comparative analysis. The lab supervisor explained that it would be several weeks before they could get to it unless it was an emergency. There was a backlog of cases and their resources were limited.

Pete continued to trap. Working along the river he could see the C-17 aircraft roaring overhead and dropping paratroopers in the drop zone directly across the river. They were dropped from various heights. Pete assumed the lower elevation drops were made as the trainees advanced in their training. As the Christmas holidays approached the paratroopers suddenly stopped jumping. Many of the trainees went home on Christmas leave.

The fur began to accumulate again. Pete decided to move some of the pelts for further drying down to the old house where he had stored the other pelts. He had been altering the diet of wild food with some of the M.R.E.'s occasionally. He had found a good hiding place for the canoe where he was now trapping. During the Christmas season, while there was so little activity on the army base, he decided to hide more fur in the old house, go back to the camp in the beaver ponds to pick up some supplies, and bring the canoe up the river in preparation for moving the trap line off Ft. Benning.

On Christmas day Pete packed up a load of green pelts and made his way south toward the old house where he had previously stored fur. The weather had warmed up considerably. The wind was from the south, off the Gulf of Mexico. Brief periods of warm weather in the winter were enjoyed by residents of the southeastern states, thanks to these southerly winds. Frequently these warm days ended when a cold air mass from the north invaded the warm air and brought torrential rain. Pete was making the most of the good weather while he could. He hiked south carrying his pack of undried fur and enjoyed the quiet woods. There were no planes dropping paratroopers, no machine gun fire or earth shaking explosions from the tank and mortar firing ranges, and no noisy helicopters. It was a good time to be alive and on the move.

Suddenly a low growl came from the brush on the left side of the road. Pete turned to look and saw six big dogs, led by a big bulldog, sprinting toward him. The growl became a roar as they came closer. Pete looked hurriedly for some escape, and saw a small sweetgum tree growing in the open woods with branches on it to a low level. He ran to the tree, dropped his pack, and rapidly climbed to a height of about fifteen feet. The dogs circled under the tree growling and snarling. The dogs were many different breeds, but all of them were large. They were wild dogs that people had abandoned or otherwise discarded. Some of them started tearing at the pack Pete had dropped. Others were looking up at Pete and trying to climb the tree.

Pete unsheathed his single action .22 caliber pistol, cocked the hammer, and took careful aim on the head of the bulldog. At the crack of the pistol the dog dropped and lay still. The other dogs looked at him but kept growling. Two more shots in rapid succession dropped two more dogs. One was kicking and snarling. By then, the remaining three took off running away. Another shot from Pete knocked one sideways, but he squealed and kept running. Pete reloaded his pistol and climbed down from the tree. A shot to the back of the head finished off the one wounded dog. The other two had been shot in the brain and were dead.

Pete retrieved his pack, and after looking around and not seeing anyone, hurried down the road As he thought about the situation he was very thankful that a tree he could easily climb had been available. Had it not been there he would most assuredly have been chewed up, or maybe killed with only a small caliber pistol for defense. The dogs had done very minor damage to the fur. Apparently no one was close enough to investigate the sound of the shots. In fact the lack of other people around may have accounted for the mood of the dogs. Pete had experienced trouble with wild dogs before, however these were the most aggressive he had seen. In the past he had caught some in traps set for fox and bobcat.

When he reached the old house on the refuge where he stored the previous cache of fur he made his way into the attic and spread out the new fur to dry. Inspecting the previous pelts, he found that they were completely dry. He removed the dry ones from the stretchers, tied them in a bundle and left them in the attic since he didn't have any better place to keep them. When more of the fur completely dried he planned to ship them to a fur buyer in New York.

After stashing the fur Pete made his way back to the hill in the beaver ponds. He was tired from a solid day of hiking. He kept thinking about the hard work he was doing running a trap line, and he wondered many times about the value of the ten pounds of white powder he had hidden in an ammo box on the Alabama side of the river. He concluded that he was in enough trouble by being falsely accused of murder. If he should be caught trespassing on Ft. Benning or trapping illegally it would be a far less serious offense than dealing in drugs. He didn't know anything about illegal drugs, but from what he had heard if the white powder was cocaine it was probably worth over $100,000.

After spending Christmas night on the hill in the beaver ponds Pete started gathering supplies to take back to his camp on Ft. Benning. He removed some of the dried, roasted corn and a little more of the deer jerky as well as a few cans of fruit. In two more weeks the deer hunting season would end on the Georgia side of the river, and he planned to move his operations back to some of the timber company land.

Late in the day of the 26th he took his supplies to the canoe, launched it into the river, and began paddling upstream. After an hour of paddling and seeing no one, he came to the small stream running through the old stand of hardwood. Turning the canoe into this stream, he left the river and was headed for his camp. The stream soon became too shallow to support the canoe. Pete waded and pulled the canoe until he came to the vine covered tributary ditch he had found for a hiding place. He packed the supplies, hid the canoe, and made his way to camp without the aid of his flashlight.

Next morning, it was still warm but becoming cloudy. The Columbus weather radio forecast rain and colder weather. Pete ran the trap line and had several animals to skin. Before he made it back to the tent the rain started. It was gentle at first, but later came in torrential, wind-driven, downpours. It rained all night and gradually tapered off about noon the next day. The clearing weather was accompanied by a biting cold wind from the north.

Pete toughed out the loneliness, and the extremes of weather. He maintained a constant surveillance of his surroundings to keep from being discovered. The little radio brought a break in the monotony. He never heard anything about the murder of which he was accused on any news broadcast. In a few more days the activity of soldiers training increased. The helicopters were flying, the machine guns were rattling in the distance, and paratroopers were parachuting into the drop zone across the river.

About a week after arriving back upriver with the canoe, he was cleaning some fish when he saw movement in the woods south of him. He hunkered down behind a tree and watched. A lone soldier was making his way in a northerly direction. Occasionally he would stop and take a sighting with his compass. He had a helmet and field pack. His rifle was slung over his soldier. Pete could see that if he kept on that course he would miss Pete's camp. The soldier was intent on the direction he was traveling and not paying too much attention to what was on either side of his route of travel. Soon he passed on out of view traveling north. Pete finished cleaning his fish and hurried on to camp.

After thinking things over he decided to take up his traps, break camp, and move off Ft. Benning. The lone soldier he saw was probably on a map and compass exercise where a course had been plotted, and he had to come in close on a final target. If this was something new, there might be many soldiers traveling through the area on different courses. This would vastly increase the probability of him or his camp being discovered.

Pete started pulling up traps and making preparations to leave. That night he cooked his fish. The flames were hidden from direct view by a wall of brush he erected around the fire. The smoke blended with smoke from controlled burns in pine stands that the timberland management people carried out almost continually during the winter on Ft. Benning.

Next morning he made several trips to the canoe with traps, furs, tent, etc. He pulled the canoe down to deeper water before loading it. By noon he had pulled up stakes and had the canoe loaded. He shoved off and was about a mile down river when a plane came over dropping paratroopers on the drop zone on the Alabama side of the river. He could see the parachutes floating down on the drop zone. Suddenly he realized that one parachute was drifting off to the east toward the river and completely out of line with the others. Pete watched as the soldier landed in the river about two hundred feet in front of him. He could see that the guy was struggling. He wasn't wearing a life preserver. He was trying to float on part of the parachute which had trapped bubbles of air. The water was cold, and it seemed to Pete there was a good chance the guy would drown if he didn't get help soon.

Well, Pete thought, I guess this is it, I can't help this guy without exposing myself, but I can't let him drown. Pete pulled the canoe up beside the soldier who grabbed the gunwale and hung on. The soldier was tangled in the parachute's shroud lines, and his teeth were chattering, Pete cut the shroud lines, and the parachute floated away. Pete said, "Easy now, lets not turn this thing over." He grabbed the soldier under one arm and helped ease him into the canoe. He covered the soldier with a poncho so he would be a little warmer, and asked him if he wanted to go down the river to a boat landing or just to the river bank on the Alabama side. The soldier said, "If I can get out on the bank over there they will probably have someone looking for me before long." Pete's initial thought was to put the soldier out and build him a fire. They headed for the river bank on the Alabama side.

Pete said, "What happened to cause you to land in the river?"

"The shroud lines on one side of the parachute got tangled, and that caused it to slip sideways instead of coming straight down. Sometimes they get tangled enough that it will cause the chute to collapse."

Before they reached the river bank they heard a boat coming at high speed from up the river. It was about twenty feet long with

67

a small deck and manned by three soldiers. The boat slowed and pulled alongside the canoe.

One of them said, "Well, it looks like you did our job for us. I see that you have a wet soldier there."

"Yeah, I guess I do. He needed help from someone. He was in trouble all right."

One of the soldiers said, "They dispatched us from the plane when they saw what happened. This has happened before so we have to stand by every time there is a drop."

Two of the soldiers leaned over and helped the paratrooper into their boat and covered him with some blankets. "We are sure glad you were here," they said. "You may have saved this guy's life." The paratrooper expressed his thanks also.

They wanted to know Pete's name and where he was from. He told them, Ruben Ware from Atlanta, and said he was taking a little vacation with some camping, fishing and bow hunting.

The soldiers sped back up the river with the wet paratrooper, and Pete hurried down the river toward the beaver ponds and his hideout on the Indian mounds. Pete considered himself very lucky that his true identity had not been revealed. He decided that there was too much activity around Ft. Benning to stay permanently hidden. He was glad he had decided to move out.

Pete hid his canoe, reset the fish trap and packed his outfit to the Indian mound. During the next few days he moved the green pelts to the attic of the old house and then spent some time deer hunting with bow and arrow on the Corps of Engineer's property which joined the river. At this point, he was just trying to kill time while waiting for the deer season to end.

One day while hunting, Pete had walked quite a distance downstream. He was directly across the river from the land owned by Jeff Callahan. This was where he had discovered the white powder hidden in the hay bales. He saw an outboard boat with two fishermen approaching from downstream. They cut the engine and pulled into the bank across the river from him. Soon two men from shore approached the boat. Pete watched through binoculars as bags were handed from the boat to the men on shore. Soon the boat left, and the men across the river disappeared. Pete was sure he had witnessed a delivery of cocaine or heroine. He wrote down the registration number of the boat. Oh, he thought, if I was only free to turn this information over to the authorities! An awful lot of evidence pointed to Jeff Callahan being involved in smuggling dope!

The following Saturday was the end of deer season in Georgia. There was a flurry of activity in the woods everywhere. It was similar to the season opening, but there was far less shooting. Hunters were breaking camp and leaving the woods until next fall. The deer weren't moving about as much this time of year. This accounted for the lessened amount of gunfire compared to opening day.

Finally, the time had come. Pete was ready to move his base of operations back to the cave. He would now try trapping on the industrial timberland to the south. He decided to first dispose of the fur he had accumulated. This was to be no easy task. The closest fur buyer was in Atlanta. He didn't want to risk a trip up there. He decided to ship the fur to a buyer in New Jersey. To do that, he must have a mailing address for the check to come to. He would have to open a P.O. Box in Cusseta under a fictitious name.

The Kudzu Vine

69

Pete inspected the fur he had left drying in the attic of the old house. He found that all but a few pelts were completely dry. Then he realized he had no material to wrap and ship them in. He tied all the dried pelts into a compact bundle then made preparations for a trip to Cusseta. He put away the camouflage clothing and dressed in casual clothes with a warm jacket and gloves. Over this he wore insulated coveralls and a helmet with goggles in anticipation of the motorcycle ride. He retrieved the motorcycle from its hiding place in the kudzu, tied the bundle of fur to the luggage rack, and tried to crank it, but the battery was dead. He waited until about three o'clock in the morning then pushed the motorcycle to the paved road going to the park and boat ramp. Once on the road he let the cycle roll down the hill and managed to crank it by engaging the gear after it picked up speed. He knew the ride to Cusseta would build up the battery. It was a cold, clear, night, and even with the warm clothes he was wearing he could feel the cold creeping through.

He had thought he would go to a trash dump behind the grocery store in town and try to find a box to ship the fur in, but in passing a place where there were three big, trash, dumpsters he noticed cardboard boxes protruding from one. He pulled in behind the dumpsters, cut off the motorcycle, and retrieved several of the boxes. He then parked the motorcycle in the woods behind the dumpsters and carried the boxes into the woods. He waited until daylight to package the fur rather than risk someone spotting a light in the woods. In the meantime he tried to sleep a little, but the best he could do was doze.

At first light he was up and soon fitted the bundle of fur into the box that fit it best. He couldn't yet seal the box because he had to enclose instructions as well as his mailing address, and he didn't have an address until he rented a post office box. Pete realized this was probably the riskiest situation he had been in since faking his death, but could not think of an alternative that wouldn't be just as risky. He had to be in town during business hours so that he could rent a post office box. The Sheriff, Walter Hooper, and the Game Warden, Joe Schodski, people he knew very well were in Cusseta, and he was very likely to bump into one of them. His only hope was that they would not recognize him with his beard and long hair. He would have liked very much to go into a restaurant in town and order a big breakfast, but that would only mean more exposure that wasn't necessary. Instead he ate some cold army M.R.E. that he brought along.

The earlier ride had charged the motorcycle battery. Finally he rode into Cusseta and straight to the post office. He removed the bulky coveralls, went inside and paid a year's rent on a post office box, in the name of Ruben Ware. He then wrote a note of instruction on where to send payment for the fur, how to make the check to Pete Lancaster, sealed the box and mailed it. He thought that when the check for the fur came he would deposit it in the account in Columbus and escape having to cash the check. He then rode the motorcycle to a truck stop on the edge of town, bought some gas, then bought a sausage biscuit and a cup of coffee.

Pete used a pay phone at the truck stop to call the sheriff's office. He enquired about the status of the case of the murder of Jessie Smith. The lady he talked to told him that as far as she knew, after Pete Lancaster drowned nothing else was done on the case. She asked who he was and he told her he was working for a reporter with the Ledger – Enquirer Newspaper in Columbus. It was almost noon when Pete headed the motorcycle back to the woods. It was time to move camp.

CHAPTER VIII

When the results of the 9MM bullet tests came back to the G.B.I. agents the results were positive. There was no doubt. The gun that fired the bullet into Jessie Smith also fired the bullet into the mobile home. James McIntire and Douglas Slagle immediately called Norma Edenview with the news.

"Norma," said Doug Slagle, "where do we go from here? Who put you onto this information? Somebody has got some explaining to do."

"Give me a little time. The guy who put me onto this said he had more information if this checked out. But first he wanted to see if the bullets were fired by the same gun. I think I can have some more information for you. Just give me a few days."

That night Norma called Joe Schodski. "Joe," she said, "just as you suspected, the bullets matched. The bullet in the mobile home was fired from the same gun that killed Jessie Smith. Now the G.B.I. agents are full of questions. I think you need to talk to them."

"Oh my God," said Joe, "I was afraid of this. O.K. I will talk to them, but first I have to consult with some other people. Let me do a little checking around and I will call you back."

"Well don't wait too long. The G.B.I. is all fired up about this now."

Immediately Joe was worried. Jeff Callahan had powerful political connections. He was rich and had befriended the right people for many years. Matching the bullets in no way convicted Jeff, in the absence of the famous "Rommel" pistol. A court trial without the pistol would only be Joe's testimony against Jeff's. No wonder Jeff "lost" the pistol on that fateful night! Of course Joe couldn't be sure of what happened either. All Joe could say was that he put Jeff out and picked him up. At this point Jeff was only a suspect, and if he told the G.B.I. what he knew they would bring Jeff in for questioning.

Jeff was on the governor's Natural Resource Committee. This committee had oversight of the Georgia Game and Fish

Commission. This agency of the state government was instrumental in setting up the game refuge where Joe worked, and the state of Georgia had started the restocking program that brought the deer back into central Georgia. At any rate, Joe knew that implicating Jeff in Jessie Smith's death would have a powerful political influence. He also knew that this influence would be directed at him if the evidence to convict Jeff wasn't present. The one lacking piece of evidence was the "Rommell" pistol.

After thinking the situation over Joe knew that he had to delay any investigation of Jeff until he had more evidence. It would be political suicide for him if the G.B.I. began questioning Jeff because of Joe's accusations. Somehow the process must be delayed until he had more proof.

Pete began packing. The industrial timberland laying south of the wildlife preserve and Ft. Benning reached for many miles in all directions. It encompassed probably 100,000 acres of the northern and western portion of Stewart County and extended into several adjoining counties as well. There were blocks of 15 – 20 thousand acres where no one lived, although the land had been densely populated and intensively farmed in the past. County maintained roads bisected a few of these tracts, and the different timber companies maintained access roads on their land.

Once the white tailed deer had been reestablished on this land and hunting seasons were opened the area became popular with hunters from far and wide. Hunters from the more densely populated areas of northern Georgia and Florida came to hunt. At first the timber companies didn't regulate hunting on their land at all. Hunters hunted where they pleased. Later the companies required hunters to obtain a permit. As hunting pressure increased the companies began leasing land to hunting clubs. Many of the clubs established hunting camps on their leases.

During the deer season hunters from everywhere were in the woods. When deer season ended the woods were a great, quiet, wilderness until spring when the turkey season opened. Except for a few logging operations, tree planting crews, and the occasional timber cruiser the forests were deserted. This absence of human activity was what Pete was counting on for him to remain hidden for a while. He felt that he could move around, hunt and trap to sustain himself, with little chance of detection. Pete had some supplies back at the cave but needed more food, clothes, and trapping supplies. He planned to make the move with two late night motorcycle trips to the kudzu patch where he had initially hidden the motorcycle then back pack the supplies from there to the cave.

Pete filled two army duffle bags with food, clothes, and traps. Late in the evening he carried these through the beaver pond, retrieved the motorcycle , and tied the bags on. He waited until after midnight to make the run toward the east. Everything went well. He hid the duffel bag contents in the frost killed kudzu and returned with empty duffel bags to the hiding place near the beaver ponds.

Next day as he was rounding up equipment to take to the cave Pete decided to go get the few animal pelts he had left to dry in the attic of the old house. As he approached the house he couldn't help but think of the poem by Joyce Kilmer.

"I suppose I've passed it a hundred times,
    but I always stop for a minute
And look at the house, the tragic house,
    The house with nobody in it."

Once again Pete climbed into the attic and rounded up the pelts. Checking to make sure he had everything, he switched on a very small flashlight that he had carried for that purpose. He didn't see any more pelts, but just before he started down, the light reflected on something metallic. He brushed aside more of the old, broken, wooden shingles and there in the dust and trash was a pistol! Holy cow, thought Pete, how in the world did that get here? At first he thought it might be the one that was stolen from him. When he got downstairs in better light he could see that it wasn't his. It was a 9MM , the same caliber as his, but a different model pistol. This was a Luger. Pete's pistol had been manufactured in Germany also, but it was a Walther P-38. This was the same kind of pistol that Jeff carried. The one he swore

74

had belonged to Rommell, the German general known as the desert fox. The gun was loaded. Pete carefully removed the clip from the gun and opened the breech removing the bullet from the firing chamber. The pistol seemed to be in good condition. Now how did that gun get there, and why? How long had it been there? The old metal roof had replaced the wooden shingles many years ago. It was obvious that the metal roof was somewhat rusty, and could have replaced the wooden shingles fifty years ago. Had the pistol been placed there by someone who lived there earlier and lost or forgotten? It was very dry in the attic. It could have remained there a long time without rusting. These questions raced through Pete's mind.

He climbed back into the attic and scratched around through the old trash and debris until he was sure nothing else was hidden there. He didn't really know what to do with the pistol. He had a lightweight .22 caliber pistol that he carried on the trap line. The only ammunition he had for this pistol was the seven bullets in the gun. This pistol would make a lot of noise when fired. He didn't need a lot of noise which might call attention to himself. He took the gun and the pelts back to the hill in the beaver pond. He wrapped the pistol in an oily rag, then put it in a plastic bag and buried it in one of the holes where he had been storing pecans and dry peas.

That night he completed the move to new territory, but not as easily as the previous night. He waited until about 2:00 A.M. to start the move with the duffel bags crammed full of supplies. He traveled east on the paved road running through the game preserve to U.S. Hwy. No. 27, then south on 27 three miles to the county dirt road running east. He traveled this dirt road in the gathering chill of the January night. Passing a few houses with barking dogs and the deer camp where his cousin and friends from the Atlanta area hunted, he soon reached the four lane Hwy. No. 280 which crossed the state from Columbus to Brunswick on the coast. A few miles south on this road was the kudzu patch which provided the hiding place for the motorcycle and supplies. There was almost no traffic at this time of morning.

With perhaps a mile to go Pete was suddenly aware of a blue light flashing behind him. He pulled off on the shoulder of the highway. A Georgia Highway Patrol car pulled over behind him. A uniformed officer got out and approached Pete with a powerful flashlight. "Let me see your drivers license," said the officer. Luckily Pete had retained his license, but the picture on it was taken long before he grew a beard. He explained this to the officer. Luckily also, Pete had bought a tag for the motorcycle. Even though it was an off road vehicle, if used on the highway it had to have a tag. Everything was in compliance with the law, but Pete's heart was pounding. He was afraid the officer would run a computerized license check, or realize that he had supposedly drowned. The officer inspected the contents of the duffle bags then told Pete he had expected to find marijuana or some other illegal drugs. Pete was very much relieved.

If it had been a local sheriff or deputy they would have recognized the name and Pete would have been headed straight for jail. Pete made it to the hiding place in the old, frost-killed kudzu and vowed to severely limit the motorcycle rides. After hiding the motorcycle he began the job of moving the supplies to the cave.

After strapping a duffel bag full of supplies to a pack frame Pete made his way through the night toward the cave. When he reached the pine forest above the cave he donned a parka from the duffel bag and lay down to sleep until morning. He wanted to wait until daylight to enter the cave where rattlesnakes could have moved in to spend the winter.

At the first light of day Pete was awake. Some coyotes were yipping and howling off in the distance, and he could hear big trucks on the highway a couple of miles to the east. He ate a hurried breakfast, donned the pack and moved into the creek bottom. Traveling up the bottom, he moved very cautiously into the cave entrance. Parting the camouflage netting and vines he peered in the cave with the aid of a small flashlight. Everything looked normal, and he didn't see any snakes. Just as he fully gained the cave entrance two squirrels ran past him and out of the cave, chattering as they went. This almost gave Pete a heart attack, but he quickly recovered.

A quick inspection of the cave found that the squirrels had chewed up some work gloves and a jacket to make nest material. The jerky, roasted corn and peanuts that had been left in large, metal containers were alright.

During the next few days Pete made a couple more trips back to the supplies hidden in the kudzu patch and completed the transfer of supplies to the cave. He began to set traps along the streams and beaver ponds in the area. The woods were absolutely devoid of people now. The only sounds were trucks on the highway to the east, some big guns at Ft. Benning, which sounded like distant thunder, and the occasional sounds from coyotes, crows and owls. The weather was cold and clear.

The cave was relatively warm compared to the outside air. Pete hung a canvas over the entrance to keep the air out, and would have liked a fire, but there was no way to dissipate the smoke. Light in the cave was from a gas lantern. Cooking had to be done outside. This was done mostly at night which lessened the chance of someone seeing smoke. The cook fire was built inside a wall of canvas, brush, etc., to keep the fire from being seen at a distance. Pete listened to the radio with his earphones while outside. He couldn't get radio reception inside the cave. He constantly monitored newscasts hoping to hear something about a break in the case of the murder of Jessie Smith.

About a mile north of the cave was a deer camp, abandoned for the season. It consisted of an open shed and some camping trailers on a high bank above a small stream. The shed had a gas cook stove and several bottles of propane gas as well as a good supply of canned food and cooking utensils. Pete came by the camp while trapping. He managed to pick the lock on the door of one of the camping trailers with his knife blade. Inside were several bunks with sleeping bags, as well as wool blankets. A closet was filled with hunting clothes and boots. A case of beer was under one of the bunks. Pete drank one of the beers and contemplated staying here part of the time. There were many camps such as this scattered through the woods, and they were all vacant at this time of year. These were certainly more comfortable than the cave. There was one problem however. He would have to be ready to vacate at a moments notice should someone arrive. People did drop by these camps from time to time for all kinds of reasons. He decided that he might visit here some but keep his main headquarters at the cave.

Similar abandoned hunting camps were scattered throughout the thousands of acres of timberlands. They were currently abandoned by the hoards of deer hunters and would remain abandoned until mid-March when the spring turkey season opened. Hunters might come by these camps from time to time just to escape the pressure of the more populated areas of the country. Also a few would come and hunt small game. For the most part the camps were abandoned until fall when preparations were made for deer hunting.

Pete strung out his trap line over greater distances now that the woods were abandoned. He stayed clear of logging and reforestation operations. His main worry now was that some lone timber cruiser might see him. Knowing that a timber cruiser or someone just walking in the woods for no apparent reason might see him kept him on his toes and always nervous. Pete thought to himself that he was living like the animals he was living with. He was always looking ahead to make sure he didn't walk up on someone, and he was always watching his back trail. He was just like the deer; constantly afraid they would be eaten.

Pete trapped mostly along the streams and beaver ponds. It was easier to hide the traps and remain undetected. In the upland he would be trapping fox, coyote, and bobcat. Traps in locations for these animals were more likely to catch someone's dog. There were some wild dogs like the ones that chased him up a tree on Ft. Benning. These needed to be eliminated, but it was too risky. If he caught someone's hunting dog or pet he was likely to be discovered.

The trap line was productive. Pete began to accumulate fur again. He skinned the animals on the trap line only bringing the skinned pelt back to the cave. There he made fur stretchers out of hickory saplings and hung them in the cave to dry. He made some more fish traps out of a small mesh chicken wire he found at an abandoned farm. At times he cooked fish in an oven at one of the abandoned deer camps. He also supplemented his diet with some of the canned goods left in the camps. He now had about a month to go until spring turkey season opened. Before that happened he would sell the fur and move back to the wildlife preserve near Ft. Benning.

Joe Schodski was worried. He was afraid he had stirred up a hornet's nest and was going to get stung. Looking back at the situation, he realized that he should have had more evidence before breaking the news to Pete's sister. However he needed to satisfy his own curiosity about the matching bullets before pursuing any more evidence. Joe wanted to tell his wife about the dilemma he was in, but he couldn't start telling her without spilling the whole story. He was afraid she might let something slip if she knew all the details.

Obviously Mr. Callahan's 9MM pistol was the missing link in this case. If it could be obtained the ballistics experts could fire another bullet and compare it to the one that killed the judge's boy. There was no use in mentioning it to Jeff again. He showed no interest in trying to find it, and Joe was sure he knew why. If it was hidden by Jeff on that fateful night he had plenty of time to retrieve it.

One of Joe's jobs was to patrol the refuge so he decided to look some more for the pistol while he was working the area. He knew where he put Jeff out, and he knew where Jessie Smith was shot. The pistol had to disappear between these two points. While he was patrolling in the area he spent a lot of time turning over rocks and logs, looking in hollow trees, etc. to no avail. It was true. Some of the area had been logged immediately after the incident. Log skidders and crawler tractors had torn up the ground. If a pistol had been laying in the grass and straw it could be completely plowed under by now. There was an old house and barn that Jeff would have passed by. Joe crawled underneath and explored them thoroughly to no avail. He finally decided it was fruitless to continue the hunt. One thing he noticed that was a striking difference from the past was the definite decrease in illegal hunting. In the past it had been fairly common for people to ride the road at night, and with powerful spotlights blind deer alongside the road and shoot them, this was a rare occurrence now. Apparently the news of Jessie Smith's death, while associated with that type activity, had been spread far and wide. Obviously, what Jeff had wanted Joe Schodski to do by shooting someone had achieved the desired results.

After several weeks of not hearing anything from Joe, Norma Edenview called him again from Atlanta. She said, "Joe , what is the deal? Are you ever going to come up with any information for these G.B.I. agents? They think they are on to something here. There obviously is a connection, but how do you establish the fact that a bullet fired into a mobile home many miles from where the boy was killed was fired by the same person? Some evidence or someone has to point out that evidence."

"Norma, I know you and the agents are growing impatient over this, but understand that I am too. I have put my best efforts at tying the loose ends together, but haven't been able to do it. When are you going to be down here again? I would like to tell you more about the situation I am in."

"I don't know," Norma responded, " We didn't have any plans to come for a while. Even though Pete is gone, if there is some evidence to exonerate his name I want to pursue it."

Joe said, "I am sure Pete didn't kill Jessie Smith too. But let me just leave it this way. Until I have some more information, the evidence is pointing to someone high on the political ladder, and it would be devastating to me and my job to open this up to investigation at this time. So please keep my name out of it. Rest assured that I am still working on this."

"O.K. Joe, I will stall them off as best I can," said Norma. "I don't want to create problems for you."

A few days later Slagle called Mrs. Edenview one evening. He said, "Mrs. Edenview have you ever come up with any more information connecting the two shooting incidents down there in Chattahoochee County?"

"I am afraid not," Norma responded. "I have tried, but I just can't come up with any answers now."

Doug Slagle said, "Well we are going to pursue this thing on our own. We are going down there and ask some questions. We will keep your name out of the investigation, but if you hear anything please let us know."

"I certainly will. And good luck to you."

Norma immediately called Joe Schodski. "Joe, the G.B.I. agents are going to come down there and start this investigation all over again. They just called and informed me. When I couldn't provide any answers to this puzzle they said they would be down to start asking some questions on their own. I just thought you would want to know."

"Oh my God," said Joe, "Knowing what I do about the situation I know that all they can possibly do is stir up trouble. I appreciate your calling me, but I don't think they will get anywhere with this. If I hear anything I will let you know. Thanks again for calling."

CHAPTER IX

The next week James McIntire and Douglas Slagle went to Columbus and checked into a motel. They were prepared to stay a while and try to find out more about the shooting of Jessie Smith. Their first stop was to visit Walter Hooper, the Chattahoochee County Sheriff, again. After arriving at the sheriff's office Doug Slagle started the conversation with Walter Hooper.

"Walter," said Doug, "You know about the bullet from Jessie Smith matching the one in Linda and Marvin Dupree's mobile home. Now we want to know whose pistol could have fired these bullets. At this point it looks less and less like Pete Lancaster did it."

Walter said, "I will just be damned if I know. I thought you guys had someone who was going to cough some more information if the bullets checked out.

" Yeah, we thought we did too, but they don't seem ready to talk just yet, so we are trying to take it from here and see what we can find out."

Walter said, "You know, I have been thinking a lot about this thing. Pete Lancaster reported his pistol stolen to the Stewart County Sheriff a month before the Duprees found the bullet in their mobile home. I really don't think we had enough evidence to arrest Pete Lancaster. Jessie Smith's daddy, being a federal judge, put a lot of pressure on ya'll to solve this thing, and I think you jumped to conclusions. You know, there are a hell of a lot of pistols in the world that fire a 9MM bullet ."

"Yes Walter, I agree," said Doug. "Since Pete is gone it would be so simple to say, `case solved,` and let this whole thing die and move on to something else. But this evidence is pointing in another direction, and we are going to pursue it. "

James McIntire, the other G.B.I. agent, broke in, "Walter, when we were here before, you mentioned a fellow named Jeff Callahan who had a place next to the Duprees. I believe you said he was an banker who owned some land in the hunting preserve where Jessie Smith was killed. You said you talked to him, and he couldn't offer any explanation of how a bullet got into the Dupree's trailer. Have you talked to him since we checked out the bullets?"

"No I haven't ," Walter responded, "I really didn't see any need to ."

"We may talk to him just for the hell of it," said Doug. "How about Joe Schodski, the game warden down there. How do we get in touch with him?"

Walter said, "I can call him on the radio if he is in his vehicle. He has radio contact with this office. When do you want to talk to him?"

"Whenever it's convenient."

Walter called Joe on the radio and told him about the G.B.I. agents who would like to talk to him. They set up an appointment to meet Joe and Walter for dinner at a restaurant that evening.

When the agents left the sheriff's office they decided to drive down River Bend Road to the park on the river. As they came to the place where Jessie Smith was killed they got out and looked around again. One puzzle they had never solved was where the shooter's vehicle had been parked on the night of the shooting. After all, this had happened more or less in the middle of the refuge. Glen Alrich, the teachers son, who was with Jessie Smith that night, could not recall having seen another vehicle at any point along the road. In the questioning of Pete Lancaster earlier he hadn't been able to recall seeing any other vehicle either. Essentially then, this meant that the person who shot Jessie had to have parked in the public boat launch area at the end of the road, or on some private land outside the refuge. Either of these scenarios would have required a walk of several miles. The other possibility was that someone who had keys to the gates on the access roads into the refuge had parked inside the refuge and walked to the point where the pistol was fired. This theory was one of the reasons

Pete was implicated in the shooting. Of course, many other forest workers, timber harvesters, etc. had keys to the gates. At this point the G.B.I. agents were just trying to think of any scenario that had possibilities.

They were looking to see how far into the woods there might be an access road when they came upon the old, abandoned farmstead. Doug said, "There had to be some kind of road here many years ago for this house to be here."

"Yeah, but I don't see any sign of one now. We need to ask Joe Schodski about roads tonight," James responded.

That evening the sheriff and G.B.I. agents met a nervous Joe Schodski at the Trails End Restaurant in Cusseta. The agents were full of questions. They wanted to know how much time Jeff Callahan spent down on the refuge? Did he have keys to the gates? They had all kinds of questions that seemed to point their suspicions to Jeff Callahan. Joe would have liked to tell them that he was riding with Jeff that night. That he put Jeff out and picked him up later. That he heard shots fired. That Jeff came back and claimed he had lost his pistol. Joe also knew that none of this would hold water. He knew that these things would incriminate Jeff, but the only thing that would convict him would be a bullet match from Jeff's pistol. This latter scenario looked less and less likely to Joe as time passed.

As they talked, Doug Slagle asked Joe, "I know Jeff Callahan did the government a big favor when he agreed to put his land into the game preserve, and I understand that he entered that agreement several years before he leased the timber rights to Great Southern Paper Co. Does he have much interest in the land now?"

"You bet he does," Joe responded, "He worries us game wardens to death. He really wants the place protected. When Pete Lancaster was here he worried the hell out of Pete, and I am sure he will worry the new fellow taking Pete's place. It's leased to the state for game management and to Great Southern for timber management, but he still wants to manage it.

Doug said, "Does he have keys to all the gates?"

"Why sure he does," said Joe. "It is still his land, and he can go and come as he pleases."

James McIntire asked Joe about the interior roads on the property.

"There is a good road system all through the property," Joe responded. "Great Southern built a good road system when they leased the property, and they keep them maintained. You could go to the Great Southern office at Lumpkin, and I am sure they would be glad for you to look at their aerial photographs. They would probably give you a map showing all the roads. What has sparked your renewed interest in this case?"

Sheriff Hooper said, "Joe, you have heard about the bullets that went into the Dupree's trailer and the one that killed Jessie Smith matching."

"Yeah, I know that," said Joe.

"Well it seems that the one that was fired into the trailer was after Pete's gun was stolen. It sure looks like someone other than Pete did this. Of course you can't rule out someone doing it with Pete's stolen pistol."

Doug Slagle said, "I think we need to talk to Jeff Callahan. We understand that he has a place out in the country near the Dupree's trailer where a lot of shooting goes on."

The sheriff said, "He's got that old German Lugar that he has bragged about for years. He said it belonged to the German general, Rommell."

Joe's heart skipped a beat. He wished he wasn't hearing this. These guys were really going to stir up trouble. Joe said, "Yeah, he carried that gun for years. I guess he still has it. I was with him one time when he shot a rattlesnake with it."

After getting the address and phone number of Jeff's bank office from Joe the agents paid for the dinner, thanked Joe and Sheriff Hooper and left. Joe and Hooper talked a few minutes outside before leaving the restaurant. Hooper said, "Joe, what are the chances that Jeff shot that boy?"

"I don't know," said Joe. "I just doubt it. If these guys want to get his pistol and fire it, Jeff is really going to raise hell. I know him well enough to know that."

"Yeah, he's got one hell of a temper," Hooper responded. " I remember one time when he ran into a fellow who wouldn't take any crap off him. He was down there logging on Jeff's property before he leased it to Great Southern. Jeff was down there raising hell with him about something, and the fellow pulled his own pistol and made Jeff get on his hands and knees and eat some grass."

"Yeah, I heard about that too," said Joe. "I guess that cooled his fever. He's going to need some more cooling if these G.B.I. agents act like they think he is a suspect."

Jeff's bank office in downtown Columbus was adequate but nothing fancy. The day after meeting with Joe Schodski and Walter Hooper the G.B.I. agents got an appointment with Jeff and went to his office to talk to him. Of course he had met the agents during the investigation after Jessie Smith was killed. Jeff was never questioned by the detectives because all the evidence pointed toward Pete Lancaster. No one but Joe knew that Jeff Callahan was in the area that night.

"So what brings you fellows back to this area now?" Jeff asked after the introductions.

"We are still investigating Jessie Smith's murder," Slagle responded.

"What do you mean you are still investigating Smith's murder. I thought it was perfectly obvious that Pete Lancaster killed him," said Jeff.

Slagle said, "We thought so too, but some new evidence has turned up."

"What kind of evidence?"

"We had rather not discuss it right now," said Slagle, "but we thought you might be able to help us."

"If I can I will be glad to," Jeff said. "How can I help you?"

Slagle said, "Does anyone who goes to your place out at Cusseta ever shoot a 9MM pistol out there?"

Jeff gazed intently at the agents and his eyes narrowed just a little. "Damned if I know what kind of gun everybody's got that goes out there. Why do you want to know that?"

"We need to test fire a few 9MM pistols," Slagle said. "Don't you have a German Lugar that shoots a 9MM bullet?"

"I lost it several months back," said Jeff.

James McIntire broke in, "Seems like a lot of these 9MM pistols got lost," he said.

Jeff began to get nervous and his face turned red. "Look you two. I don't know what you are driving at here. I lost my pistol while riding my horse down there on the property several months ago. I had been riding a good while and rode up on a rattlesnake. I reached for my pistol and it was gone. The holster was unsnapped and it had fallen out somewhere. I went back and looked for it, but never could find it."

"Did you have it insured?", Slagle asked.

"Yeah I did, but I had such a high deductible I didn't file a claim. Look, you two are barking up the wrong tree if you think I had anything to do with shooting that boy. I can see what you are thinking. Now you get the hell out of here. I am busy, and I don't want you back in here. If you come back again you better have a subpoena. Now as far as I know, this case was solved long ago. You better just let the sleeping dog lie."

James and Doug left and realized they had no basis for getting a subpoena. They also realized that no help was to be forthcoming from Jeff. In fact, finding their investigation at a dead end, they decided to return to Atlanta.

Doug said to James, " I was planning to get a court order if necessary, to test his guns, but no use to do that now."

"Yeah," said James, "He either hid it or lost it. Anyway, we aren't going to get it now."

CHAPTER X

Pete was about ready to wind up the trapping season. It was the last of February. The weather was getting warmer. Red Maple and wild plums were blooming. Small, purple flowers in the low weeds of meadows and abandoned fields carpeted large tracts of open land. Old, abandoned home sites became very colorful from the blooming of trees, shrubs and flowers planted long ago. Some of these, such as pear trees, yellow jasmine – a vine with small, yellow blooms, and jonquils – a yellow buttercup that sprouted from bulbs every spring, continued to bloom many years after the houses were gone and trees reclaimed the land. There was always concern that early blooming fruit trees such as peaches, pears, and plums would be damaged by freezing weather. Some years these fruit crops were destroyed by late freezes.

Pete had already taken up his traps. He was waiting for the last of his fur to dry completely before making another trip to Cusseta to mail the fur. After he sold the fur he planned to move back to the hill in the beaver pond on the game refuge. Spring gobbler season would open in about two weeks, and this would bring hunters into the woods again increasing the chances he could be caught. Listening to a Columbus radio station, he learned that yesterday set a record for heat so early in the season. The temperature hit 83 degrees. Pete knew this couldn't last long at this time of year. The next cold front would probably bring torrential rain and the threat of tornados.

The doves were cooing and wild turkeys were beginning to gobble. Pete decided that while he was waiting a few days for his fur to finish drying he would try to trap a wild turkey. He had never done it but thought he could. He cut some wild cane growing in a stream bottom near a beaver pond. The native cane was similar to bamboo but much smaller. It was about three quarters of an inch in diameter and fifteen to twenty feet in height. Pete cut the stalks into short pieces and tied them together to form a shape similar to a pyramid which stood about two feet high. He planned to place this on the edge of a corn field where turkeys had been feeding on left over corn. He would dig a hole under one side big enough to admit a turkey and bait it with corn. If the turkey acted like other birds he had trapped when the turkey got inside he would try to find an exit while looking up but would never go out the way he had come in. At least that was the theory. He knew that quail traps built on that design worked and he thought that it would work for turkeys too.

Pete had carried the trap to the edge of a field and was preparing to set it when he saw someone running through the field. Pete crouched in the brush at the edge of the field and watched. He was wearing camouflage so it was easy to hide. The fellow crossed the field where Pete had walked earlier and continued on at a steady jog disappearing into the woods. Suddenly Pete realized that the man was wearing a prison uniform. The pants were a dull white with a blue stripe down each leg. The shirt was white with blue trim also.

Pete waited and watched a long time trying to think the situation through. He was over a mile from a public road. Most of the land in the area was wooded with a small percentage of farm land interspersed. If the man he had seen earlier was an escaped convict the authorities would certainly be looking for him, and he didn't want to get caught in someone else's war. As he sat in the brush contemplating his next move he heard some hounds baying in the distance. As he waited, the sound of the barking dogs came closer. Finally he saw the dogs approach the old corn field. There were three of them held by uniformed police officers. Two more men with shotguns backed up the dog handlers. The dogs seemed to get confused down where the escapee's trail crossed Pete's.

That was all Pete needed to see. He took off running through the woods to the north. The escapee was moving toward the west. If the dogs had actually picked up Pete's trail instead of the escaped prisoners and stayed on it he could easily determine the dog's direction in a little while. After running about half a mile to the north Pete stopped to rest and listen. Sure enough – the dogs were on his trail. He thought about what he could do to throw the dogs off his trail. He could head for a creek or beaver pond and try to lose them by getting in the water. Then he thought about the rope he had hidden on the edge of a canyon. This was a couple of miles to the north and in the direction he was headed.

Unknown to Pete a work detail of state prisoners were trimming brush on the right-of-way of a state highway a few miles to the south. They were guarded by a man with a shotgun. At some point the guard had been distracted and one of the most dangerous prisoners had slipped into the brush and ran away. The guard called for the search party and trail dogs. It didn't take them long to get there. In the meantime the Georgia Highway Patrol, game wardens, sheriff's department, etc. were engaged to patrol or stand guard on all the roads surrounding the area where the prisoner escaped.

Pete jogged along through the woods to the north making his way to the rope on the edge of the canyon. He hadn't planned to be out long so he had no supplies such as food, water or extra clothes with him. He had the .22 pistol, waterproof matches and a pocket knife so he wasn't burdened in his travels by extra gear. Pete had been a fugitive before, but now he had the genuine feeling of being a fugitive. What sorry luck! He really thought that when trail dogs homed in on a particular scent they stayed on that trail without fail. He never expected to get caught in a situation such as this. Occasionally he could hear the baying of hounds far to the south but still on his trail.

When he reached the canyon where he had hidden the rope he wasted no time retrieving it from the stump hole. He looped the rope around a good solid pine tree on the brink of the canyon, wrapped the double strand of rope around his waist and between his legs then rappelled down the side of the canyon. When he reached the bottom he pulled on one strand of the rope and retrieved it from above. He then walked on rocks to a small stream. Entering the stream, he was careful not to touch either bank. He was trying not to leave any scent to be picked up by the tracking dogs. He knew it would take a quarter mile detour around the wall of the canyon for the dogs and their handlers to reach the bottom.

Pete headed downstream. The water was cold and soon his boots and legs were soaked. It was getting late in the day and turning cloudy. The stream was running west and soon entered a larger creek. Pete was getting cold and tired, but there was no alternative He had to keep going. There was some concern that the warm weather would have brought water moccasins out of hibernation. He thought about the possibility of snakebite as darkness came on, but again, there was no alternative.

After wading the larger creek for a couple of miles, just before dark he came to U.S. Hwy. 27 which ran north and south. The creek passed under the highway flowing west through a large concrete culvert. He could see a highway patrol car parked on the side of the highway up the hill from the creek. A patrolman was no doubt in radio contact with the search team as he watched to see if anyone crossed the highway. Brush and trees lined the creek banks on both sides of the creek. Pete was careful not to make any noise as he approached the culvert. Emerging on the west side of the highway, he continued downstream. A quarter mile west of the highway Pete decided he had been in the water long enough. He felt like he had safely eluded the tracking dogs.

As he emerged from the creek he found a forest road paralleling the creek. It was almost totally dark now and Pete didn't have a light. Thinking about his situation, he decided he wouldn't have used a light if he had one. Someone might see it.

The wind blew from the southwest. The lightning flashed and thunder rolled. The rain that Pete had been expecting accompanied by cold air from the northwest was upon him. The clouds obscured the moon and stars. He could make out the outline of the road but just barely. Before long Pete was completely soaked by the rain. His feet had been wet a long time, but now all his clothes were wet, and he was cold. He could only make out the outline of the road from the flashing lightening. It was pouring rain. The wind was blowing, and as he slogged along down the muddy road he didn't know where he could take shelter from the storm. Normally he would have had a small survival pack with him which contained a waterproof poncho, some military

91

M.R.E.'s, a compass, and waterproof matches. He had always carried this on the trap-line, but this day he neglected to bring it. Of course he had the .22 pistol which he always carried.

Suddenly in a flash of lightening he saw a large pile of logs, two log skidders and a hydraulic log loader. The loader was attached to a truck tractor that was used to move the loader. The cab of the truck tractor was unlocked, and Pete crawled inside. He stripped off his clothes and wrung the water out of them. A roll of paper towels in the truck cab helped him to dry off. He managed to turn on the interior light and saw some old, greasy coveralls, and some gloves that someone had left. He put his damp clothes back on as well as the coveralls. Pete sat in the truck cold, hungry and exhausted as the rain continued to pour down. At least, he thought, the trail dogs were out of business now.

Sometime during the night the rain stopped, but the wind blew furiously bringing in cold air from the north. The wind blew so hard it shook the truck tractor. Pete was so cold he couldn't sleep. He would have liked to crank the truck and run the heater, but there were no keys. He ripped up the rubber floor mat in the truck and took the coarse, fiber padding from under the mat. By wrapping up in the floor covering material and lying on the truck seat he gained some warmth and managed to sleep a little – more from exhaustion than from comfort.

At dawn's first light Pete replaced the floor mats and left the truck wearing the coveralls for extra warmth. Being careful to avoid leaving footprints, he eased out of the area and headed west. The logging crew would probably return before long. The temperature was below freezing. Ice had crusted on the puddles left from the rain. The wind steadily blew from the northwest. Pete knew that as long as the wind blew from that direction it was bringing in colder weather. Once he cleared the area where he spent the night he kept a brisk pace into the wind. The forest road soon ended, and the area of industrial timberland extended fifteen miles to the west where it intersected river bottom farmland along the Chattahoochee River. Brisk walking warmed him as he traveled through a combination of natural woods and various ages of planted pine. He traveled on firebreaks, deer trails, and dim woodland roads.

After a few miles he came upon an abandoned hunting camp. There was an open shed with a gas stove, propane bottles, and a long table. Several trailers were parked nearby. It was obvious that no one had been there for a good while – probably since deer season. One of the trailers was unlocked. In it he found a pair of shoe pacs – leather boots with rubber bottoms. In a drawer were several pairs of wool socks. The wool blankets on a bed looked comforting, but he knew he had to keep moving.

Another trailer was locked. Pete was desperate for something to eat. He took a long, flat piece of iron and managed to pry the door open. He opened some curtains to let light in. In some cabinets in the kitchen area he found several cans of fruit juice, soup and other food. The kitchen had a gas stove. It didn't take him too long to get the stove lit and some soup warming. He lit all four burners and enjoyed the warmth. In a closet he found a wool army shirt as well as insulated underwear. After eating, he dressed in the insulated underwear and wool shirt, the coveralls, wool socks, and pac boots. In a duffel bag he packed his damp, dirty clothes, old boots, one of the wool blankets, a sheet of plastic, some canned food, two boxes of matches, and a bottle of whiskey. He was a lot better prepared to make it back to his camp on the hill near the river now.

As Pete trudged along with the bag heading west the northwest wind blew steadily. This late, cold weather was unexpected, but not all that rare. Coming on the heels of record breaking warm weather is what hurt. It had caught him off guard and he suffered the consequences. His mind raced back as he pondered the situation. He wondered what had become of the escaped prisoner. Did he remain free, or was he recaptured? He didn't have his radio so couldn't pick up any news. He thought back over his months on the run. The recent incident, the time the cop stopped him on the motorcycle, the misplaced paratrooper at Ft. Benning; all were incidents fresh on his mind. It added up that no matter how careful he was, it was quite possible that sooner or later, quite by accident, someone would discover his identity. Although he wasn't guilty of anything the fact remained that he had jumped bail.

What must I do, he thought? He considered trying to get a false identification such as drivers license, social security card, etc. and reestablishing himself in some other part of the country.

When McIntire and Slagle returned to Atlanta they talked to their boss, and related their failure to make progress on the case. They were very frustrated. Doug Slagle called Pete's sister.

"Norma," he said, "you have got to know a lot more than you are telling us about these guns and bullets and the people involved. Now we have been down there working like hell trying to find out who did kill Jessie Smith. If you want to clear up Pete's name you are going to have to help us."

"Doug, all I have done is pass along some information that was given to me. If it hasn't helped I am sorry, but I am still not at liberty to divulge who gave me the information. I think that in time I will be able to tell you, but right now I can not. I am sorry," Norma explained.

Doug said, "Well if you get any tidbit of information that you are free to share for God's sake give me a call. At this point we know that there is an unsolved murder, and we need a break in this thing somehow."

"Don't you worry," replied Norma, "If anything breaks I will let you know."

That evening Norma called Joe. "Joe, what is going on down there? There has to be some reason why you suspected that the bullet in the Dupree's trailer matches the one that killed Jessie Smith. The G.B.I. is coming down hard on me. They know that someone has the connecting link in this mystery. They think it's me. Now Joe you have to tell us more."

"Listen," Joe said, "I am working my butt off trying to get this thing straightened out. Just stay cool for a little longer. I think I will have something soon. Please bear with me."

After this Joe redoubled his efforts. He spent more time on the refuge. He knew in his own mind that Jeff Callahan had been the person who shot Jessie Smith. He also knew that without Jeff's pistol to compare the ballistic tests to there was no incriminating evidence. Joe was convinced that the G.B.I. was making matters worse by trying to contact Jeff.

After the G.B.I. agents talked to Jeff he realized that a cloak of suspicion had been cast upon him. The more he thought about it the more nervous he became. He thought more about the German luger pistol that he had hidden in the attic of the old farm house. What if someone should find it. He knew that would be his undoing. Jeff decided that he would retrieve it and either destroy it with an acetylene torch or throw it in the river. He didn't want anyone to see him in the area where Jessie was killed so he didn't park on the highway and walk to the old house. He went in a gate and took the road that he and Joe had been on the night he killed Jessie Smith. Driving as close as he could to the old house, he parked and walked through an area recently burned. Great Southern Paper Co. had done a lot of control burning in pine stands this winter to improve wildlife habitat. The fire had gone close to the old farmhouse. Firebreaks had been plowed around the house however to insure that it wouldn't burn.

When Jeff reached the old house he entered and climbed the ladder which was made into the wall of the closet beside the chimney. Reaching into the attic, he groped around in the debris on the floor of the attic for his pistol. He couldn't feel it. He retrieved a small flashlight from his pocket and probed the darkness in vain in search of the pistol. He finally realized it was not to be found. Someone had beat him to it! "Now who the hell could that have been?" he thought.

Reluctant to leave without the gun, he finally gave up and dejectedly trudged back toward his pickup. Just as he reached the truck Joe Schodski drove up.

Jeff said, "Well I see you are still on the job."

Joe responded, "I'm picking out some places for wildlife biologists to put in research plots. They want to see how much deer browse comes back after a control burn on different soil types. They plan to put in the plots and remeasure them periodically. What brings you back here?"

"Oh, nothing much. I was just wandering around. I was looking at the heart pine lumber in that old farm house back there. I would like to have some of that lumber. I had two years to remove any buildings when I leased the property, but now it belongs to Great Southern. They would probably still let me get the lumber though."

"Did you ever find the pistol you lost", Joe asked?

"No I never did. With all the activity around here – cutting timber, control burning and all – no telling where it is now. I gave up looking for it. Well, I've got to go now – see you later."

After Jeff drove away Joe wondered what his real purpose for being there was. After all, he thought, this was the very place they had parked the night Jessie Smith was killed. He noticed that Jeff seemed nervous. He wondered if the G.B.I. agents had touched a nerve and prompted him to make some foolish move.

When Pete arrived back at his hideout on the game refuge he dug out the hip boots, waded into the beaver pond to the hill and started digging out supplies to make the place livable. He erected the tent, built a fire, warmed and ate some canned food that he retrieved from metal cans and plastic bags he had buried underground. He poured a small glass of whiskey. Sitting by the fire and sipping on the whiskey he contemplated his next move.

His radio was left behind at the cave, so he could not hear any news or weather reports. The remainder of his fur and many other items that he would have brought back under more normal circumstances were still in the cave. And of course his motorcycle was still hidden in the kudzu patch over there. He knew that he must return soon, retrieve the fur and other items, and sell the fur. After that he thought he would somehow try to obtain some false identification and leave the area. He was becoming very tired of living as a fugitive. However, he knew that if he left he would always be a fugitive, but thought he would stand less chance of being discovered.

After a few days the weather warmed considerably. The wild turkeys were gobbling and he could hear more boats on the river as the number of fishermen increased. Turkey season was open now which meant that the hunting camps would be occupied again, and camouflaged turkey hunters would be in the woods. Any traveling off the refuge would have to be done with care because hunters were in the woods again. Game wardens such as Joe Schodski were on the lookout for hunters who might be poaching on the refuge. This meant that Pete had to be very careful on the refuge. Turkey hunters weren't nearly as numerous as deer hunters, and they usually didn't stay in camp for extended periods, but especially at the first of the season they were an element to be reckoned with.

Pete's food supplies were beginning to run low. The deer jerky, peanuts, pecans, parched corn and dried apples that he had so carefully preserved were about gone. He still had some emergency army rations and a few canned goods. There was no wild fruit to be had and no produce from farms this time of year. The fish trap provided some bream and catfish. Grease to fry fish was running low so they were baked in a reflector oven made from aluminum foil. During short trips to fish or check on the fish trap he noticed some fresh sigh of wild hogs.

Pete took a small .22 caliber survival rifle that had been stored at the camp and decided to try to shoot a wild pig. The rifle came apart for easy storage. The barrel and receiver fit into a waterproof chamber in the plastic stock. Pete dug it up, unwrapped it from the plastic bag he had stored it in, and attached the barrel to the stock. The gun was a semiautomatic with a clip that held nine bullets. He loaded the clip with .22 magnum bullets, left the beaver ponds and eased along parallel to the river in search of wild hogs. He was traveling north – toward Ft. Benning, but still on the game refuge.

Pete heard a hen turkey clucking. Then far to the north he heard a turkey gobble. As he approached the area where the hen was calling he suddenly realized that it wasn't a hen at all but someone calling the gobbler! Suddenly he saw some movement

97

and recognized the form of a person very well camouflaged, sitting next to a big oak tree. He had a bow and arrows and was looking in the direction where the tom turkey was gobbling. Pete froze in his footsteps and then softly backed away from the area. At first he thought that the person was poaching then realized that he was on the narrow strip of land owned by the U. S. Army Corps of Engineers that ran parallel with the river. The Corps granted permits to archery hunt only, and this hunter very likely had a permit.

Pete knew he was taking a chance shooting even a .22 caliber rifle in the area. A game warden in a boat on the river would know that a rifle shot in this area would mean that someone was violating the archery only policy of the Corps of Engineers or that they were hunting illegally on the game refuge. He decided that the risk was worth taking if he could get a hog. He thought that the possibility of a game warden hearing him was pretty remote anyway. At any rate the turkey hunter ended his hunt this morning.

Pete decided to get out the canoe, do some fishing and keep the .22 rifle handy in case he should see the wild hogs. He killed several days doing this and late one afternoon he saw some hogs leave a sandbar and climb the river bank downstream from where he fished. He beached the canoe then pulled it up the bank into the brush and set off to intercept the hogs. He could hear them grunting and rooting around. He cautiously eased into the area where they were feeding. He picked out a medium size pig and aimed for his ear. When the rifle fired the pig collapsed and the others went running. The bullet had entered the pig's brain just behind the ear and killed it immediately. Pete smiled as he remembered an old army colonel, a doctor and another guy he had hunted wild hogs with in south Florida some years ago. They called themselves the "Order of the Ear". They strived to shoot a hog in a spot that the bullet hole could be touched with the hog's ear. The accurate bullet placement meant no suffering by the pig and immediate death. There was no chasing of wounded hogs.

Pete covered the pig with leaves and straw then backed off to wait a while and see if the rifle shot attracted anyone's attention. After a wait of 30 minutes or so with no sign of any other person in the area he went back to the canoe and retrieved a plastic garbage bag. He then cleaned and skinned the pig. He cut off both hams, the tenderloin from the back and some pieces of shoulder meat and placed this in the plastic bag.

Arriving back at camp after hiding the canoe, Pete set about to cook the meat – perhaps 25 pounds of pork . The weather was warming so there was no hope of preserving it for long. He decided he would eat it as fast as he could. It would be a welcome change from an all fish diet. He built a fire with oak wood to create some live coals. He then wrapped the hams in damp cloth. He placed some live coals in one of the holes he had dug to hide supplies. Covering the coals with a thin layer of dirt he then placed the wrapped hams in the hole and covered them with a thin layer of dirt and added more coals. He then filled the remainder of the hole with dirt. In effect, he created an underground oven to bake the ham. He fried some of the other meat to eat immediately. The remainder of the meat he sliced into thin strips and smoked on the rack where he had made the venison jerky. The next day he dug out the hams and they were thoroughly cooked.

As the month of March ended most of the trees except oak and hickory were putting on new leaves, ducks and geese were flying north, the days were longer and the weather was getting warmer. Tulips and jonquils were blooming at old house places and the dogwood trees were beginning to bloom.

Pete decided to make a trip back to the cave to retrieve the fur and other items. He decided to go at night in the middle of the week when fewer hunters were in the woods. Thinking of the dogs that had interrupted his travels at night in the past he decided to better prepare himself in case he was attacked. Of course he could always shoot an aggressive dog, but that would attract attention that he didn't want. Pete always carried a knife and the .22 pistol for whatever emergency might arise. He knew that he would not use these weapons against anyone to keep from being captured, but he would certainly use them to protect himself from animals such as the wild dog attack at Ft. Benning. He didn't want to be captured and face prosecution for a crime he didn't commit, but he certainly wasn't going to commit a crime to keep from being captured. He was in enough trouble already, through no fault of his own.

Pete cut a small hickory sapling about five feet long. To one end he secured a small diameter cable and ran it through a series of staples to the other end of the stick. On the opposite end where the cable was secured he had some slack cable. He carried this as a walking stick with the secured end toward the ground. He thought that if a dog should attack he could make a loop with the cable on the end of the stick, catch the dog's head in the cable loop and choke him into submission very quietly.

Pete left the beaver ponds around midnight. He had a pack with a little of the smoked pork and parched corn, a first aid kit and the rappelling rope that he planned to hide again. He also had his .22 pistol and knife as usual and a small flashlight and the walking stick for bad dogs. As he passed the place where Jessie Smith was killed it touched off bad memories of that night over six months ago when he happened on the scene.

Pete reached Moccasin Gap in the middle of the night. As he passed some houses he attracted some dogs' attention. They came out to the road and barked but didn't try to attack him. Farther down the road a beagle and a Doberman pinscher came running out. As they reached the road the beagle stopped, but the big Doberman came on. He didn't bark. He just emitted a low growl. Pete readied his stick. He made a loop with the cable. As the dog reached him he lifted the stick and whacked him on the head as hard as he could swing the stick. Pete intended to put the loop over the dog's head and choke him if necessary, but the dog collapsed and lay still after the lick on the head. Pete quickly dragged the dog to the shoulder of the road and continued on his way.

By the time he reached the cliff where the rope was hidden it was getting daylight. He put the rope back into the same stump hole where he had placed it earlier. He carefully proceeded toward the cave watching and listening for any sign or sound of turkey hunters. He saw no hunters, but could hear tractors running as farmers prepared the land to plant their crops.

When he arrived at the cave he ate some of the smoked pork and opened a can of fruit. Pete was very tired after walking all night. He slept most of the day.

The next day he removed the last of the raw fur from the stretchers. They were well dried now. He listened to the news on the radio again while he packed the fur and other items to be packed out to the motorcycle. Pete wasn't sure that he would ever be back so he packed a good many items. It took two trips to the motorcycle to get all the items out.

After the second trip to the motorcycle he tied the stuff on as best he could then still had a good load in a backpack as well. He made sure the motorcycle would crank then waited until late that night to make the trip to Cusseta. He eased the motorcycle on to the highway at about 2:00 A.M. remembering the last time he had the motorcycle on the highway and got stopped by the highway patrol.

The dumpsters where he found boxes to pack his fur in before yielded no packaging material this time. He continued on to Cusseta and found some empty boxes behind a grocery store. He was afraid to package the fur in the light from the security light behind the store. His actions would look suspicious to anyone who saw him at night. He broke the boxes down and traveled back down the highway a couple of miles then eased off the highway and into the woods to wait for daybreak. After daylight he made two packages of fur and addressed them to the fur house in New York.

After 8:00 A.M. he went back on the road to the post office. He mailed both boxes and checked his P.O. Box for mail. There was nothing but some junk mail because no one knew his address. In fact no one he had known in the past knew he was alive so they certainly didn't know his assumed name.

After this he ate a good breakfast at the truck stop and filled his motorcycle with gas. He went to the grocery store and bought oranges and bananas as well as some canned fruit and vegetables. His diet lately had been sorely lacking fresh fruit.

Pete rode the motorcycle back down to River Bend Park. A couple of vehicles were parked there hooked to boat trailers, but no one was in sight. Pete rode the motorcycle into the kudzu patch where he had hidden it before and started packing supplies to the hill in the beaver pond. He was thinking that in two weeks he would pick up his check for the fur at the post office, and deposit it in his account at the bank. He would then catch a bus to St. Louis, stay there a few days then catch one to Denver. From there he would go to Jackson, Wyoming to spend the summer. He planned to purchase a different ticket at each stop, thus making it harder for him to be traced.

As April wore on the weather became warmer. Pete began to make preparations to leave. It seemed that there was no point in staying here and risk being found. It seemed that sooner or later someone would stumble onto his true identity. He decided to make one more trip to Cusseta, pick up his fur money and prepare to leave. Before doing that he washed all his clothes using a method he discovered long ago. He filled a five gallon milk can about half full of dirty clothes, then some washing powder and water. He tied this can with a wire and sank it in the river's edge under a lot of floating debris. This was in an area where no one would be fishing because of the overhanging tree limbs and the debris floating on the water. The wave action from passing boats constantly agitated the milk can and its contents. The clothes were completely clean by the end of the day and only had to be rinsed and dried. He took the clothes back to the mound in the beaver pond to dry. It was a very efficient and effortless way to wash clothes. Pete had no way to iron. He just shook the wrinkles out as best he could. Where he had been spending his time, wrinkled clothes were the least of his worries.

Pete decided there was no place he could leave the motorcycle in town without it being stolen or traced to his ownership. He rode to Cusseta on the motorcycle late one night and checked a suitcase full of clothes into a locker at the bus station. He then ate breakfast at the bus stop. He picked up his mail and decided to call one last time and inquire about the status of the murder of Jessie Smith. According to the people Pete talked to, nothing had changed. He had a check for $850 for his fur. He rode to Columbus and deposited the check.

CHAPTER XI

Pete rode back to the kudzu patch to hide the motorcycle. He had already decided to leave the motorcycle in the kudzu patch, and leave the canoe in the ditch near the river. He didn't know what the future held and knew that he might need them in the future. He took the small tag off the motorcycle and stuck it in his pocket. In the event someone found the motorcycle, they wouldn't be able to trace the tag to his ownership. Next he drained all the gasoline out of the tank. He kicked the starter to crank the engine and drain the remaining gasoline from the carburetor which would better prepare the engine for storage. The engine backfired with a loud pop then started running. Suddenly Pete was standing in a lake of fire! All he could do was run. The backfiring engine had ignited the gasoline fumes from the emptied tank! The flames were about knee deep and covered a radius of about 30 feet from the motorcycle. Pete left the motorcycle running and leaped to safety. Luckily he escaped before his clothes caught fire. The fire ignited the tinder dry, frost cured kudzu, and flames began to leap high into the air. There was no hope of extinguishing the blaze. The motorcycle ran for a few seconds and stopped. It had consumed the gasoline in the carburetor. It was in the center of the fire with flames 20 feet high now.

The only thing that Pete could do was run. He knew that stopping the fire was hopeless. At this time it was a given that the entire kudzu patch was going to burn, and probably a lot of woodland too. Pete ran toward the beaver ponds. He had seen kudzu burn before. It was more like an explosion than a fire. The many years' accumulation of dead leaves and vines provided a tremendous amount of fuel. After frost killed the vine in the winter it burned like no other fuel. His concern now was to get out of the area before someone saw him. It was hard to run in kudzu vines, but Pete was making time. He could hear the fire roaring up the hill behind him.

Joe Schodski was down close to the river on the game refuge. It was the 23rd of April. The Grancey Greybeard, a shrub sized plant, with long, streaming, grey flowers was blooming. The oak leaves were half grown. Pecan, hickory and muscadine vines were leafing out now. The woods had a soft look with all shades of light green leaves. Joe was thinking how lucky he was to have a job that put him in close touch with nature. He was quietly admiring the scenery while looking and listening for poachers. He suspected that people were sneaking onto the refuge from the river to hunt turkeys and deer. In fact this activity had been reported to the state law enforcement office and passed on to Joe.

Suddenly Joe thought he heard a gun fire and an engine crank. He knew it wasn't a boat motor on the river. It sounded like it came from the big kudzu patch. He ran to the edge of the kudzu and could see smoke rising. He caught a glimpse of someone running toward the river. He considered trying to catch him then realized it was useless. He would have to cross the entire kudzu patch, which probably covered 50 acres and the person he saw was on the other side and into the woods. Joe ran back to his truck and called the sheriff's office. He reported the fire and urged them to get the Ga. Forestry Commission fire suppression unit on the way to River Bend Park pronto.

Joe unlocked the gate on the road that ran toward the kudzu patch and waited on the highway for the Forestry Commission truck carrying a crawler tractor with a fire plow. Joe watched as the fire intensified and black smoke filled the air. It took 20 minutes for the truck to arrive. Joe knew the operator of the unit whose name was Jim Duke.

Joe said, "Jim, you might just want to pull through the gate a little ways and unload your tractor. That thing is burning in a kudzu patch and really raising hell. I hope you can stop it. I don't think you want to park the truck too close."

Jim said, "Yeah I'll just walk the tractor down there. I may have to call for another unit if it gets too big."

Jim unloaded the tractor and took off for the fire. Joe drove his pickup back down the road toward the fire. He could see that the fire had already burned out of the kudzu and into the woods on the uphill side. The fire wasn't nearly as intense after leaving the kudzu. Jim's plowed firebreak was stopping the fire in the woods. Jim continued to plow around the fire as Joe watched. When Jim reached the downhill side of the fire the blaze was still out in the kudzu, but he made no attempt to plow through the kudzu. He continued with a firebreak in the woods at the edge of the kudzu. This allowed the flames to die down and go out when they reached the break.

"How did this thing get started," Jim asked Joe.

" Damned if I know," Joe said. "I was pretty close to the kudzu when I heard a noise out in the kudzu patch. When I went to have a look I saw a fire and a man running toward the river. I don't know what was going on. When this fire gets cooled down I'm going to have a look out there where it started and see if I can find anything."

"Well if you do find something let me know," said Jim. "I'll have to turn in a report. It looks like it will have to be classed as incendiary."

"Yeah," Joe responded, "not much question about that,"

Jim said, "I have to put the acreage burned in my report too. What do you think about 50 acres?"

"That looks good to me," Joe responded. "I noticed you didn't try to cut it off in the kudzu."

Jim said, "I learned a long time ago to stay out of kudzu with a fire plow. You can't stop a fire in kudzu with a 50 foot break. It's useless to try to stop it with a little old fire plow making a break about five feet wide. Besides that, you can fall into a gully that's completely hidden by kudzu. That's why the kudzu is here in the first place you know. It was planted in gullies to control erosion. Of course it didn't stay in the gullies. It's everywhere now."

"You might call the office of Great Southern at Lumpkin when you get back," said Joe. "They will need to make a fire report on it too I think. Don't think it burned anything much but kudzu though."

"Yeah I'll give them a call." said Jim. "Are you going to stay on down here for a while?"

Joe said, "Yeah I thought I would stay a while and see if I can figure out just what happened here."

"Well if you need us just call," Jim said. " And if you get a better handle on how this started let me know. I think I will load up and head on back."

Joe hung around until late in the day without seeing any sign of human activity. He decided to go home and come back in the morning to see if he could find out anything more about the fire.

When Pete reached the beaver ponds he dug out his hip boots and waded to the hill. Back in the direction of the kudzu he could see the black smoke rising. What sorry luck, he thought. Well one thing was for sure, no one would catch him riding the motorcycle now. He already had most of the things he would take on his trip in a locker in Cusseta. He had planned to walk to Cusseta the next night and catch the bus.

Now Pete could hear the crawler tractor running in the distance and knew that someone was fighting the fire he had inadvertently started. He never dreamed he would ignite gasoline fumes by starting the motorcycle engine, and was very thankful he didn't get burned.

Pete busied himself packing the remaining items into the backpack he would take on the trip and placing the other items in underground storage. He decided he would keep the .22 pistol in his check on luggage.

The next morning he took down the tent, rolled up the sleeping bag and put them in large plastic buckets. He then put the buckets inside plastic bags and buried them in the Indian mound. He reflected on the possibility that he may never get to see the Indian mound excavated. Pete had all day to kill since he wasn't leaving until dark to walk to Cusseta. He put on some old boots and coveralls and decided to have a look at the motorcycle to see if it could be salvaged if it should ever be needed. He knew he would have to walk through the ashes and soot. If it was any good at all he thought he might place it in a gully and let the kudzu vines grow back over it.

Joe Schodski had a burning curiosity about the noise he had heard and the mysterious fire in the kudzu patch on the game refuge. He got up before daylight the next morning. At an early hour he was back at the scene of the fire. Since he had seen someone running from the scene the day before, he thought that they just might have left something important and would return to get it. The fire was completely out now. As soon as he could see good he headed for the spot where the fire started.

The kudzu patch was a completely different place after the fire. There were a few scorched trees that had been covered with kudzu vines. All of the ditches were exposed now. As Joe approached the area where he first saw the fire he saw something protruding from the blackened mess. It was a burned motorcycle! The motorcycle was still standing upright on its stand and burned completely black. The tires were burned off, some plastic parts had melted and all the insulation had burned off the wiring. The key was still in the ignition. There was some old junk which had been placed in the gullies years ago and covered by kudzu, but Joe could tell that this wasn't junk. He knew it had been a good motorcycle before the fire.

Now, Joe wondered, what in the world would possess someone to bring it into a kudzu patch, and who was that someone? There was no tag that could be traced. He started looking for a serial No. and finally found it stamped into the frame. It could possibly be traced that way, he thought. There was nothing else to indicate ownership. There were a few tools lying around the ashes.

Joe thought it just possible that someone would return. He decided to wait a while and see. He picked out a spot in a gully close to the motorcycle behind some scrubby burned trees. He went back to his truck and picked up a folding stool, a thermos of coffee and a magazine that he kept for just such an occasion.

Joe had been sitting there for about an hour when he saw a figure leave the woods down below and head in his direction across the burn. He crouched a little lower in the ditch as he watched the guy coming toward the motorcycle. Joe could see that the man was wearing camouflage army fatigues and boots. When he got closer he could see a pistol in a holster on his belt. He looked very much like a soldier except for a full beard. He approached the motorcycle with purpose so Joe knew that this wasn't a chance encounter by some wandering stranger but was undoubtedly the person who started the fire yesterday. He looked vaguely familiar, but Joe didn't recognize him. The man stopped and looked around then concentrated his attention on the motorcycle. Joe approached him silently through the ashes of the kudzu to within 20 feet. He drew his pistol and told the man to freeze and put his hands up. Pete jumped and started to run, but when he saw the pistol in Joe's hand he stood still and raised his hands. Joe approached and relieved Pete of his pistol. Pete recognized Joe immediately, but Joe still didn't recognize Pete.

"What are you doing here?" he asked Pete.

"I was just looking at where this fire burned," Pete responded.

Joe began to evaluate the situation. This man could only be charged with trespassing. Even though he was carrying a .22 caliber pistol there was nothing to indicate that he was hunting.

"Is that your motorcycle?" said Joe.

"Well it was," said Pete "until it backfired and caught this dead kudzu on fire, and I had to leave it. Joe, you don't know who I am do you?"

"No I don't guess I do. What's your name?"

"Pete Lancaster."

Joe didn't say anything for a while. He looked at Pete who still had his hands in the air.

Pete said, "Take that billfold out of my back pocket and look at the driver's license."

Joe did as Pete asked and there was Pete's driver's license with a picture of Pete before he grew a beard.

"Well I'll be damned!" said Joe. "I recognize your voice now. I knew something about you looked familiar. Well put your hands down. Damn, I can't hardly believe this. However I had my doubts all along. Let's go up here out of these ashes and talk. Don't worry I'm not going to run you in."

Joe handed Pete his pistol, gathered up his stool and other belongings and Pete followed him uphill out of the burned area to Joe's truck.

Joe said, "Pete, how in the hell did you pull this off? And what in the world were you doing down here on a motorcycle?"

"Well Joe, first of all I didn't shoot Jessie Smith."

"Yeah, I had about figured that."

"Well I just made up my mind that I wasn't going to prison for something I didn't do. I hid some supplies here in these woods, then faked the drowning. I was trying to buy some time and maybe find out who did actually shoot that boy. Say – Joe, you aren't going to turn me in are you?"

"Hell no," said Joe, " I had already figured out that you didn't shoot Jessie Smith. You mean to tell me that you have been in these woods ever since last fall?"

"Well, here and some other woods too. Look could we move off this road to do our talking. I keep worrying that someone may drive up and see me"

"Sure," said Joe.

Joe got a couple of soft drinks out of a cooler on the back of the truck and handed Pete one.

"Let's move right up here. I want to hear this story."

From this point on Pete spent the next 30 minutes telling Joe what he had done. He really unloaded on him. It was good to have someone he could trust and who believed in him. Joe just let him talk and occasionally interrupted to ask a question. Pete emphasized all through the conversation for Joe to please keep quiet and not let it slip that he was alive.

After a while Joe began to tell his side of the story. He told about putting Jeff out of the truck the night of the shooting. He had never told anyone this. Then he told Pete about the G.B.I. and the matching bullets, and his suspecting that Jeff did the shooting. But there was no tying it all together without Jeff's famous

German Luger. He told Joe about Jeff losing the Luger the night Jessie Smith was killed.

The news of the missing Luger hit Pete like a bolt of lightening!

"My God," said Pete! "I may have found that pistol. You see, back in the winter when I was trapping, I dried my fur in the loft of that old house. When I was getting my fur out I found a Luger 9mm pistol. I figured it would make too much noise for my needs so I hid it in the Indian mound."

"What Indian mound?"

"Joe, that hill in the middle of the beaver ponds is an Indian mound."

"Hell, I didn't know there was a hill in the beaver ponds."

"Yeah, well I found it a couple of years ago. Not many people ever go into those beaver ponds I am sure. That's why I figured it was a good place to hide. It's about a quarter mile back from the river. There's this little hill that pops up out in the middle of the ponds. I've got my camp in there. I never dreamed it was an Indian mound until I dug up an Indian bowl while burying some supplies.

"So that's where you have been hiding?" asked Joe.

"Yeah, part of the time."

"Look, we need to get that pistol to the G.B.I. and let them check it out. If it matches the bullet that killed Jessie Smith then I believe we have found the guy who did the killing."

"Yeah, and I believe he is involved in drug trafficking too, but that's another story. Look Joe, I was just before leaving. I was going to catch the bus and leave town tomorrow. In fact that's why I drained the gas out of my motorcycle. I had already checked my suitcase in a locker in the bus station in Cusseta. Here's the key to the locker. How about you getting my suitcase and turning in the key. And here's $20.00 How about bringing me a loaf of bread and something to make sandwiches with. I will get the pistol and meet you back here tomorrow."

Joe said, "Boy! I stopped you just in the nick of time didn't I? I guess it would be a good idea for you to stay hidden until we get all this checked out. Your sister knows about the matching bullets. She is going to be mighty surprised. But don't worry, I'm not going to breathe a word of this until they get the bullets checked out. Damn, I hope that is the right gun. O.K. I'll see you about 10:00 tomorrow if nothing happens."

That night Joe wanted to tell his wife what was going on, but knew that he didn't dare tell anyone.

Pete went back to the Indian mound and dug out the supplies he had just hidden. He erected the tent and made preparations to stay a little longer.

The next morning Joe bought the sandwich making material Pete requested. He then retrieved Pete's suitcase from the rented locker at the bus station and turned in the key. He put the suitcase in the big toolbox on the back of his truck so that no one would be able to see it and ask questions. He then went back to the truck stop and bought a cheeseburger, French fries and a coke for Pete. He started thinking about some place Pete could stay without hiding out in the woods. He thought about it a while, but could not come up with a better plan. At least until the gun was checked out by the G.B.I., there was probably no safer place for Pete to be.

At 10:00 A.M. Joe pulled into the woods on the road approaching the burned kudzu. Joe locked the gate behind him. After about ten minutes Pete approached the truck from the woods where he had waited to be sure no one was following Joe.

Pete had the Luger pistol and a clip that still had seven bullets in it. He was real happy to get the cheeseburger, French fries and coke.

After seeing the pistol Joe said, "Yes sir that looks like the pistol old Jeff carried and swore it belonged to Rommell."

"Yeah, I saw him with it all the time," said Pete. "It just didn't dawn on me that it could be Jeff's when I found it in the old house. Of course I didn't know he was in the area that night. Even if it checks out to be the gun that killed Jessie Smith, how are they going to prove that this was Jeff's gun?"

"I don't know. I can testify that he had the gun when I put him out, and he didn't have it when I picked him up later. I hadn't thought about it, but that still doesn't prove beyond a reasonable doubt that this was his gun does it? Well, first let me get it to the agents to check out. Are you going to stay in this area for a while?"

Yeah, I guess I will. The mosquitoes and deer flies are starting to get bad though. I may have to find some higher ground to get away from them."

"Well I will get this pistol to the G.B.I. agents. They really want to move on with this case. Hopefully they will complete the tests soon."

Joe and Pete then rigged up a system whereby they could leave messages for each other. They agreed that if either of them had a message for the other they would tie a small piece of flagging tape to the gate then put a written message in a plastic bag under a rock down the road from the gate. They would both try to check the gate once a day to see if there was a message.

Pete headed back to the beaver ponds with his suitcase and Joe headed for town with the pistol. He started to go to the sheriff's office, but decided instead to contact the G.B.I. directly. He called the office in Atlanta and managed to talk to Douglas Slagle.

"Doug," said Joe, " You remember that pistol we were looking for to see if it was the one that fired the bullet at Jessie Smith?"

"Yeah, sure I remember."

"Well, I have a pistol that we strongly suspect as being that gun."

"Where did you get it?"

"I can't say at this point where I got it. I just want to get it to you to have it tested. Can you do that?"

"Sure we can do it. That's what we have been wanting to do all along. Boy you are going to have a lot of questions to answer if this thing checks out. You know that don't you?"

Joe asked, "How can I get the gun to you?"

"Why don't you meet me half way today. We will have the lab do this right away."

It was about a two hour drive from Columbus to Atlanta. They agreed on a meeting place where two highways crossed and Joe headed north.

Boy, they really do want to test this pistol, thought Joe. Well we should have an answer to this puzzle soon.

When Joe met Doug at the meeting place he made Doug sign a receipt for the pistol, complete with gun Serial No. before he would let Doug have it. He also told Doug, "I can't explain the situation right now, but it is very important that you get this test done fast."

"I intend for it to be done fast, or I am going to kick some butt. I'll call you as soon as I get the results," said Doug.

On the way back to Columbus Joe thought about telling the sheriff what he had done. After all, Walter Hooper was the person who had requested help from the G.B.I. initially. He also thought about calling Norma in Atlanta. He then decided against any of the calls deciding instead to await the lab results.

Pete was elated with the latest turn of events. At last, he thought, some progress was being made. He was thankful that he had not left the country. Of course everything depended on how the pistol checked out in the tests. He had eerie feelings about how they could prove that the Luger pistol belonged to Jeff if the tests proved positive. In the meantime he must carry on with making a living and remaining undetected, but he knew that it was a matter of time before his luck ran out. In fact that was why he had decided to leave. He also knew that his luck would have been vastly different if he had been found by anyone other than Joe Schodski.

Pete thought about dragging out the canoe and doing some fishing. A lot of fishermen were on the river now. He really didn't want to run the risk of having his license checked by some game warden who might recognize him. He also considered a trip in the darkness down river and across to the old barn where the dope was hidden. He decided that might turn into an extended trip. He wanted to stay close to check the gate for the possibility of a message any day. He decided to lay low, use the fish trap, and fish from the bank a little. He would stay close by and wait for the test results.

CHAPTER XII

When Doug Slagle got to Atlanta with the pistol he went immediately to the lab that had checked the bullets earlier. The lab supervisor was a middle aged red headed lady named Shirley. Doug said, "Look Shirley, I know you folks are busy and you probably have a backlog of cases to work on, but I need this done now."

"Well, we are behind schedule. If you are in such a hurry you can help. We have to have a witness to the testing in case we have to testify in court."

"Yeah, I will help. What can I do?"

"Come with me down to the firing range. We'll shoot the bullet into some cotton, retrieve the bullet and compare it to the one that killed Jessie Smith to see if it has the same marking on it."

"Now that's the kind of action I wanted," said Doug. "Where is the firing range?"

"It's just down the hall. Come on we'll do it now."

They walked down the hall and entered a soundproof room. They each donned hearing protectors. As Shirley watched, Doug loaded and fired the pistol into a large basket of cotton. Shirley turned on an X-ray scanner to locate the bullet and they retrieved it from the cotton. They returned to the lab and retrieved two bullets from the file. One had been retrieved from Jessie Smith's body and one from Marvin Dupree's trailer. They gave the bullets to a technician who immediately began checking them under a microscope. Doug sat in an office outside the lab and tried to read a magazine while they examined the bullet. He was so anxious about the outcome of the examination he couldn't concentrate on reading.

Finally Shirley approached him. "Well," she said, "the technician says there is no doubt. All these bullets were fired by the pistol you brought us."

"Thank God," said Doug.

" We will put the bullets with the pistol and keep them in the file here until they are needed at the trial. We will write up a complete report on the findings. Who should we send the report to?"

"Send it to Walter Hooper, the sheriff of Chattahoochee County and send me a copy. Hey - many thanks for doing a rush job on this."

Doug tried to call Joe Schodski but couldn't reach him. Later that evening he called Joe at home.

When Joe answered the phone Doug said, "Well Joe we got it checked out already and it matches. This was the gun that fired the bullet that killed Jessie Smith, and it's the same one that fired the bullet into the trailer. Now we need to know whose gun it was and where it came from."

Joe had already thought the situation through thoroughly. He wasn't ready yet to let the detectives know that Pete Lancaster was alive and well. He would tell them about his activities during the night Jessie Smith was killed, and tell them he had found the pistol in the old house where Jeff Callahan had hidden it. He knew that some proof of ownership of the pistol had to be established, and he wasn't going to expose Pete until they had the noose around Jeff's neck.

"O.K. I'll see if I can set up a time when we can get together."

Early next morning Joe was at Walter Hooper's office. Joe wanted to talk to the sheriff before the G.B.I. called him to set up a meeting. When Hooper came in Joe told him he needed to speak to him in private. They went into an inner office and Joe began to fill Hooper in on what had happened the night Jessie Smith was killed. He told him about finding the pistol, about the ballistics lab check etc.

"My God Joe," said Hooper, "why didn't you tell about putting Jeff out when we had the initial investigation?"

"Because I just didn't put two and two together, I guess. I never slightly suspected Jeff until much later when we got to talking about his lost pistol. That got me to thinking – then when you mentioned the bullet in the Dupree's trailer I thought it was just possible that it might check out."

"Well we have a mess on our hands now. How are we going to prove this is Jeff's pistol?'

"I don't know. Maybe we can get some ideas from the prosecuting attorney or the G.B.I.'

When Joe left he headed straight for River Bend Park. He wrote a brief note to Pete about the pistol checking out, put it in a plastic bag under the rock and tied a piece of ribbon on the gate.

Later that day when Pete checked the gate from the safety of the woods he saw the ribbon. Anxiously he backtracked to the rock and retrieved the note.

As per the prior agreement no name of to and from were on the note in case, by some remote chance, someone else should find the note. The note read, "We were right. The gun checked out. Now we have to establish ownership of it. Meeting soon with G.B.I., sheriff, prosecuting attorney, etc. They don't know about you. Just lay low for a while."

Pete thought, well I know how to do that. I have been "laying low" for a long time now. I can do it a little longer. His heart jumped with joy. At last, there seemed to be a break in the case. What a fortunate turn of events! This had happened when he was in the depths of despair. He had all but given up and was so close to leaving the country. Well there was nothing to do now but kill time and wait. He was sure that if he needed anything he could leave a note for Joe and it would be provided. He removed the ribbon from the gate to let Joe know he had found the note. He determined to stay close by and wait for more news.

Doug Slagle started making calls to the prosecuting attorney, Walter Hooper and Joe Schodski's boss. Wednesday of the following week was the earliest date they could all get together. Of course Joe's schedule was very flexible. He could meet almost any time. Doug called Joe and informed him of the meeting date.

Joe's boss, Alan Hancock, was in Atlanta, the headquarters office of the southeastern region, U.S. Fish and Wildlife Service. Mr. Hancock was in charge of law enforcement. This included law enforcement on all federal lands in the Southeast. It also included enforcement of federal wildlife regulations as they interconnected with state wildlife regulations.

Mr. Hancock called Joe. "Joe, what is this meeting all about?"

Joe said, "Do you remember when that judge's boy was killed while he was out night hunting for deer last year down here?"

"Yeah, yeah I remember that all right. That was on the management area just below Ft. Benning wasn't it ?"

"Yeah that's the area I patrol so much you know. Well we have come up with some new evidence of who killed the boy. I am involved in this thing, and I requested that you be at the meeting. If it goes to trial like I expect it to I am going to be tied up in court a lot. I just wanted you to be informed."

"Well I thought they had it figured out that the forester with Great Southern shot the boy."

"Yeah, they thought they had it figured out, but now it looks like they were wrong. Anyway it should be an interesting meeting, and they will explain the evidence they have."

"I will see you there then," said Mr. Hancock as he hung up the phone.

Joe figured that he should let Pete know the meeting was a week away and see if there was anything Pete needed. He drove down toward River Bend Park later that day, left a note under the rock requesting a meeting with Pete at 10:00 A.M. the next day, and tied another ribbon on the gate.

Joe drove into the woods the next day and waited. After a short wait Pete appeared. He told Joe how pleased he was to find out about the bullets matching. Joe had brought along a sack full of groceries for Pete. He told Pete who all would be at the meeting next week and that he felt sure they would decide on a strategy for proceeding with the case. Pete told Joe that he would kill time by taking his canoe down the river and across to the Alabama side to check on the dope smuggling. They agreed to meet at the same place next Thursday when Joe could relay the

117

result of the meeting to Pete. Of course Joe cautioned Pete to be extremely careful.

Pete gathered a few camping and fishing supplies and prepared to paddle the canoe downstream at night. He took along the jungle hammock for sleeping. The weather was getting warmer all the time. The hammock let the air circulate through the protective mesh which kept insects out.

It seemed at this point that Jeff Callahan was definitely the person who shot Jessie Smith. Pete was fairly certain that Jeff was involved in smuggling drugs also. He just wanted to check and see if the operation was going on as before.

Sometime after midnight Pete eased the canoe out on the Chattahoochee River. He made the two mile trip downstream without incident. He paddled up the small stream that entered the river from the west, and found the same hiding place where he had stashed the canoe before. This was on the edge of the 1,000 acres of Jeff Callahan's planted pines where Pete had discovered the stash of dope. Pete hung the jungle hammock and crawled in for some much needed rest.

Next morning he unloaded the canoe and hid it in the same ditch where he had hidden it before. He made a camp in the thick, planted pines a good distance from the river and ate some M.R.E.'s for breakfast. Before fishing or anything else he set out to check the old settlement with extreme caution. Remaining in the cover of the woods, he surveyed the scene around the old buildings for a long time. He checked the entrance road and found that it had been used, but not since the rain. Finally he eased up to the old barn. Upon entering the big owl flew out the hole in the back. Old bales of hay were still in place. He counted twelve bales. On the back of the stack he picked out a bale, untied the twine it was bound with, and opened it up. Sure enough, he could see packages of white powder in plastic bags. He retied the strings and quickly exited the building. This was enough to tell him that the operation was still ongoing.

The wild plums and dewberries were ripe now. Pete gorged himself on them. The dewberries ripened a couple of weeks ahead of blackberries.

Pete retrieved his fishing gear and headed for the river. He checked on the status of the white powder he had stashed in the ammo box near the old dead oak tree. It was still there.

Upon reaching the river bank he picked a place to fish so that he couldn't be seen from boats on the river. The bream were bedding now and Pete had all the fish he could eat in about 30 minutes.

On Wednesday, the day picked for the meeting of all concerned at the Chattahoochee County Sheriff's office, Joe Schodski arrived early. Joe was anxious. He knew that some people would not want to believe that Jeff Callahan was a suspect in the killing of Jessie Smith. Well, Joe thought, all I can do is tell it like it is and let the cards fall where they will.

When all the members had gathered, the group consisted of Joe Schodski – game warden, Walter Hooper – sheriff, James McIntire and Douglas Slagle – G.B.I. agents from Atlanta, Allen Hancock – Joe's boss from Atlanta, and Bill Adams – the district attorney who would prosecute the case if it went to trial.

Walter Hooper started the meeting by making sure that everyone was introduced. After that, Joe took the floor and explained in detail what happened on the night Jessie Smith was killed. He explained how he had put Jeff out and picked him up later after hearing shots being fired, and how Jeff had reported his pistol being lost. This was a real eye opener to everyone but Hooper to whom Joe had already explained his activities that night.

Joe's explanation of the activities taking place on that eventful night brought questions from everyone. Like the sheriff, they all wanted to know why he had not reported these events sooner when the initial investigation was ongoing.

"I guess I was just a dumb ass," Joe responded. "But it just didn't occur to me that Jeff had time to travel that far after I put him out. And when he came back and reported hearing the shots that I heard I guess that just cinched it for me in my mind that some other people were doing the shooting."

"When did you finally become suspicious that Jeff might have done the shooting?" asked Doug Slagle.

"Well, I don't know for sure," said Joe. "Later I just got to thinking about it, and in talking to Jeff he didn't seem too interested in finding his pistol. I guess that fact alone got me to thinking."

Joe's boss, Mr. Hancock, asked Joe "Why do you allow Jeff to ride with you when you are patrolling the area?"

"Well it just happens on rare occasions. But after all some of this is his land. I guess the political clout he has is something we wanted to keep on the good side of."

"Yeah, I think I see your point."

The sheriff then asked Doug Slagle to explain the bullet testing. Doug explained that they had the 9MM bullet recovered from the autopsy of Jessie Smith. Then he explained how Norma Edenview, Pete's sister in Atlanta, had requested that they test the bullet recovered from the Dupree's mobile home.

At this point, Joe interrupted and explained how he had become suspicious of Jeff, and upon hearing of the bullet in the Dupree's mobile home thought it very possible that it came from Jeff's pistol. Joe explained how he didn't want to become involved at that point, and how he got Pete's sister, Norma, to contact the G.B.I. about testing the bullet.

Doug Slagle said, "After the bullets matched, and we couldn't get an explanation of this from anyone, we came down here and started asking questions. We got an interview with Jeff but didn't learn anything. When we got to pushing him about the location of his pistol he explained that he lost it while riding horseback. We asked him if it was insured and he said that it was, but he didn't file a claim."

Doug continued, "Some time after our trip down here Joe found this pistol in an old house on the refuge very near to where Jessie Smith was shot. We tested a bullet from that pistol and it matched the other two. In other words, this pistol was the murder weapon."

Bill Adams, the district attorney, asked, "What proof do you have that this is Jeff's pistol?"

"That's where we are right now, "Slagle explained. "We need to find out where Jeff's pistol was insured. I imagine they have the serial number recorded. If they do, that would verify if this is Jeff's pistol."

Mr. Adams said, "See if you can find out who carries his gun insurance. I think your case is good enough that we can get a court order to examine his insurance records if necessary."

With that, the meeting ended. It was now up to the G.B.I. to examine the insurance records. The district attorney said they would issue a warrant for Jeff's arrest if the pistol tested was his.

The day after the meeting Pete was in the woods waiting for Joe's truck to arrive. Joe reached the meeting place about 9:00 A.M. Pete watched the truck to make sure Joe was alone. He then approached the truck and got a full report on the outcome of the meeting. He also gave Joe a report on the continuation of the drug smuggling he had observed on the Alabama side of the river. Joe had also brought along a few more groceries for Pete.

Pete said, "I sure hope they can find a serial No. for that pistol. If they don't, then there's no way to prove whose it is."

"Well I sure hope so too," said Joe. "In the meantime about all you can do is lay low. Is there anything I can get you?"

"I need a few things. I eat a lot of fish. Bring me a sack of cornmeal and five pounds of sugar and a gallon of cooking oil. I may move my camp. The bugs are getting bad around these beaver ponds. How about some insect repellent too?"

"Well check the gate every couple of days," said Joe. "As soon as I find out something about the gun I will let you know. Meet me here Saturday morning and I will have your groceries."

CHAPTER XIII

In Atlanta James McIntire and Doug Slagle pondered how to find out who Jeff had his insurance with. They didn't want to try for a court order at this point. They feared that Jeff would start hiding information. They had determined that Jeff was a gun collector. Different people had told them about Jeff's rare gun collection. He had exhibited these at gun shows in the past. They felt sure that with so many guns he would have them insured someplace.

Mr. McIntire told Slagle that he had a friend who was an insurance salesman. "I think we could get this salesman to go down there and meet with Jeff and try to sell him some insurance. In the course of the conversation he could probably find out who Jeff has his insurance with."

"Yeah, he could probably do that by comparing rates, etc. Tell you what though before we do that let me call some gun collectors I know and see who they have insurance with."

McIntire agreed and Slagle made several calls to gun shop owners and collectors.

What he found out was that a good many gun collectors had insurance with the National Rifle Association. People had to be members of the N.R.A. to obtain this insurance. The N.R.A. didn't require the listing of serial numbers for guns unless they had exceptional value. The very expensive guns were listed separately along with their serial numbers. Doug Slagle got a phone No. for the N.R.A. and called them. He enquired as to whether Jeff Callahan had insurance with them. The lady on the phone told him that they had no record of a Jeff Callahan. This came as some relief to Slagle since a serial No. might not be recorded if his insurance was with the N.R.A.

At this point Slagle and McIntire agreed to let the insurance salesman try to gain some inside information.

On Saturday morning Pete met Joe to get his groceries and insect repellent. Joe had something else for Pete too – a fully charged cellular phone. They agreed that Pete would turn it on for ten minutes at 6:00 every evening. That way the battery should last a long time. If Joe had any important information for Pete he could contact him and Pete wouldn't have to hang around the river bottoms all the time. It was agreed that Pete wouldn't call Joe unless it was an emergency.

"I don't believe you are going to have to hide out much longer," said Joe. It shouldn't take them too long to find out where Jeff's insurance is and to see if that gun is on his policy."

"Well I sure hope not. I don't want to be on the run forever. I appreciate this phone. I think I will be up in the hills for a while instead of on the river. Call me every few days so I can see if this thing is working. If it quits, I will come down and put a ribbon on the gate."

"O.K., I'll be patrolling the river more now. I'll be in touch. You be careful."

It was the last of May. Wild plums and dewberries were plentiful. This food along with greens from dandelions, green brier tips, and poke salad as well as fried fish provided plenty to eat.

Pete decided to get up in the hills for a few days. He didn't want to leave the area and go back to the cave. He decided to take some supplies and cross the river then go up in the hills on the Alabama side of the river.

At six that evening he turned on the cellular phone. A few minutes later Joe called and Pete told him his plans. The next day Pete packed some supplies onto a pack frame. He broke out the canoe and made ready to cross the river, but waited for the cover of darkness to do so. Once on the river he thought about going down to Jeff's property. He decided against that for several reasons. He knew the place was being watched by law enforcement from Alabama, Georgia, and maybe the F.B.I. too as a result of his information to Joe. He also wanted to be close to the management area on the Georgia side as he awaited information from the ongoing investigation of Jeff Callahan's gun serial numbers. He also wanted to be up in the hills where there weren't so many insects.

Pete made a very short trip almost directly across the river and pulled the canoe up a small creek on the Alabama side. He strung up the jungle hammock and crawled in for some sleep, thankful for the netting that kept the mosquitoes out.

Early next morning Pete awoke and tried to find a ditch off the small stream to hide the canoe in. He couldn't find a ditch so he dragged the canoe up the bank of the small stream, cut some brush, and covered the canoe. He ate a hurried cold breakfast as the mosquitoes and deer flies buzzed around his head. He then shouldered the pack frame and headed uphill.

In the river bottom the elevation was about 250 feet above sea level. On the highest hills in the area elevation approached 700 feet. Most of the original homes built by European settlers were up in the hills. When the trees were cleared, these areas caught more of the summer breezes, which helped to control insects and cool the houses.

Pete trudged through the mixed pine-hardwood forest. He crossed a county dirt road and came to a large open pasture. He skirted the open pasture staying in the woods and continued to gain elevation. Finally he found what he was looking for. At the top of the hill about an acre of hardwood trees projected out into open cropland. From up here he could see the surrounding country for a long way, and he could already notice the breeze and the absence of insects. To the north lay Ft. Benning and the parachute drop zone. To the south steam rose from the paper mill perhaps 15 miles away. To the east, on the Georgia side of the river, there was wave after wave of tree covered hills. There was some farmland in the area where he was located and a few miles downstream there were a few farms in the bottom land on both sides of the river.

Pete set up camp among the trees at the top of the hill. Aware that a light could be seen for a long way, he had to be very careful with a cooking fire. The trees on the hill top were a perfect target for lightening too. In the event of a thunderstorm he would hurriedly abandon the hill top.

Back in Atlanta at the G.B.I. office McIntire and Slagle debated their next move. There were other cases that demanded their attention, but like a hound on a hot trail, as the likelihood of catching their prey became nearer reality the more excited they became.

"Doug, let's get this buddy of mine, Kimborough Buchwald, to go try to sell Jeff Callahan some insurance. I know he can at least find out who he has insurance with."

"I think that might be a good move," said Doug. "What kind of insurance does he sell?"

"He sells all kinds," said McIntire. "Let me see if I can get him on the phone."

They got Mr. Buchwald whom they called Kim to come over to the G.B.I. office. The agents explained what they were after. All they wanted at this point was to find out what company Jeff had his gun insurance with. To keep from arousing any suspicion, they instructed Kim to concentrate on life, liability, and other insurance and casually mention guns. After all, they said, you might sell him some insurance, but we just need to know who he has his gun insurance with.

Kim called Jeff's office and determined that Jeff would be there the next day. Early the next morning he was on his way to Columbus. He was a blonde headed, fair skinned young man in his early 30's. He had worked at several different jobs since graduating from college, but when he tried selling insurance he knew he had found his niche. He had a gift for emphasizing a person's need for insurance.

Arriving at Jeff's office a little early, Kim struck up a conversation with his secretary. He explained to the middle aged lady that he represented an international company that sold all types of insurance including life, liability, farm and home, shipping, travel, etc.

"Because our company is international in scope and does such a large volume of business we can offer premiums cheaper than any company," proclaimed Kim.

At this point he had about convinced the secretary that she needed to switch to his insurance.

"By the way, who does Mr. Callahan have his insurance with at the present – or do you know?"

"Yes," replied the secretary, "He has his land insured with Farm Bureau Insurance. He has quite a lot of farm and timberland you know. He has errors and omissions insurance for his law practice with another company, and I don't know anything about his life insurance.

Kim was a skilled listener as well as talker. He was thinking that he could possibly combine all of Jeff's insurance under one umbrella policy at a better rate than he was now paying.

Presently Jeff came into the reception area.

"I don't have a hell of lot of time to waste – especially talking about insurance," he said as his eyes glared at Kim from under his bushy, gray eyebrows.

Kim replied, "After talking with your secretary I see that you have several kinds of insurance with different companies. The advantage of my company is that we sell about every kind of insurance imaginable. We can probably combine all your policies under an umbrella policy and furnish you a huge savings. I would like to talk to you a few minutes about it."

"Well come on back, but I don't have long."

Kim followed Jeff to a back office. They sat down and began to talk. Jeff mentioned the types of insurance he had. He couldn't remember the exact coverage and premiums of all the different policies but could tell from Kim's quotes that he could probably save money by combining his policies. Kim definitely had his interest.

"What about guns," Kim said. Someone told me that you were quite a hunter and gun collector. Are they covered by your home owner's policy?"

"Yeah, they are covered under the Farm Bureau policy. I have all of them listed. I had to get up all the make, model and serial numbers. They gave me a cut rate because I have them in a big walk in safe built into my basement."

"Which Farm Bureau office do you deal with?" asked Kim.

"I deal with the office in Lumpkin."

After some skillful maneuvering by Kim, Jeff agreed to have all the information on his insurance coverage and premiums together and meet with Kim again next Monday. Kim assured Jeff that he could save him some money.

As he drove back to Atlanta Kim knew that he had the information that James McIntire and Doug Slagle wanted. When he arrived at the G.B.I. office Kim sat down with them and told them what he found out.

"The guns are covered under what sounds like a special rider included in his home owner's policy with the Farm Bureau in Lumpkin. They are listed along with the serial numbers from what he said."

"Well boy you sure came up with the information we needed," said Doug.

"I'm going back down there next Monday," said Kim. "He is supposed to have all the information together so I can give him a rate for our insurance. I may be able to get a list of the guns with the serial numbers."

"Well we could probably go to the Farm Bureau office in Lumpkin and look at his policy," said Doug. "But rather than stir things up lets just wait and see what Kim comes up with."

"Yeah," said Mr. McIntire, lets call Walter Hooper and tell him what we know. If Kim can't get a list of the guns next Monday we will need to go to the Farm Bureau office in Lumpkin."

Of course neither the G.B.I. agents nor Walter Hooper had any idea that Pete Lancaster was anxiously waiting in the bug infested woods for an answer to the question of ownership of the Luger pistol. When Walter Hooper received the call he relayed the information to Joe Schodski. That evening Joe relayed the information to Pete Lancaster in his 6:00 P.M. phone call.

Pete was delighted that progress was being made. It seemed that he might soon cease from being a fugitive. From this phone conversation he knew that it would be at least one more week before they had a definite answer to the ownership of the gun. Until this was determined there was nothing to do but lay low.

Hiding out, on the run, laying low – these were the things he had been doing since last September. What was he to do? Pete couldn't just sit there and watch the corn grow. He had to be doing something. All hunting seasons were over now. No hunters were sitting quietly in woods with a sharp eye for any movement. There was little chance he would be seen if he moved around carefully.

The next day Pete took some fishhooks and line and started toward a farm pond he could see about one half mile away. As he made his approach to the pond he walked inside a pasture fence. The walking was much easier there where grazing animals had eliminated the underbrush. Suddenly he thought he heard a low growl. He stopped and focused his attention out in the pasture. A big brahma bull was heading toward him and bellowing as he came. When the bull was about 50 yards away he stopped, shook his head, and pawed the ground with one front foot. Pete slipped rapidly through the barbed wire fence and went out of the bull's sight into the woods. The bull came on to the fence and stopped, still bellowing and raising hell. Pete thought the bull probably weighed a ton and if he had been mad enough could have come through the fence as easily as a bulldozer.

Pete continued toward the pond but stayed out of sight of the pasture so he wouldn't excite the bull. The incident with the bull reminded Pete of an incident that happened to a friend and coworker some years earlier. The man was going deer hunting on some timberland over behind a large pasture. He was taking a shortcut across the pasture and was about half way across when he heard the thundering of hooves coming toward him. He looked around and saw a big, mean bull with his head lowered coming directly at him as fast as he could run. The guy looked around hurriedly for some means of escape. There was nowhere to go and no tree to climb. There was no possibility of reaching the fence at the edge of the pasture before the bull caught him. He did the only thing he could do. He took aim with the 30-06 rifle on the bull's head and squeezed the trigger. When the rifle fired the bull collapsed in a big pile in the middle of the pasture. The fellow took off running out of the pasture and forgot about deer hunting. Of course he should not have been trespassing in the pasture, but in order to save his life he shot the bull. He then told the bull's owner what happened so the meat could be saved, and it stirred up quite a controversy. Pete had remembered this story told to him by his friend. He also remembered that somewhere he had read or heard that more people were killed by domestic cattle each year in the United States than by any other animal. He thought about all this as he headed toward the pond and decided he would stick to the thick woods instead of open pastures from now on.

When he reached the pond he remained hidden among the trees along the backwater of the pond. He fished with worms and caught several bass and bream. He cleaned the fish then proceeded through the woods back to his campsite on top of the hill.

Pete hung around the area for several more days. He picked blackberries, wild cherries, plums, wild greens and roots to supplement the fish and a few canned foods he had. The 6:00 P.M. phone calls provided no news. After five days he broke camp and headed downhill toward the river and the hidden canoe.

When he reached the spot where he had hidden the canoe, it was gone. Nothing was left but the brush he had cut to cover the canoe. After a thorough search of the area it was obvious that someone had found it, and it was gone. Damn, Pete thought, of all the lousy luck! He knew a ditch was a better hiding place, but he just hadn't been able to find one at this location. Well one thing was for sure, he couldn't swim the river with all his gear. He had to build a raft.

Pete remembered seeing large pieces of Styrofoam caught among driftwood in places when the river flooded. He set about looking for some and found two good size chunks. It had obviously been used for boat docks someplace upstream in the past. Working out of sight of people on the river, he cut driftwood poles about eight feet long and tied these to the Styrofoam blocks. His original intention was to sit on top of the poles out of the water and paddle the raft across the river. He soon realized that the contraption was too top heavy for this and would dump him in the river. He decided to turn it over and kneel in the space

129

between the Styrofoam blocks to paddle. This would mean getting wet, but it would get him across the river. Whoever found his canoe got his life preserver and paddle too. He fashioned a rough paddle out of a board found in the driftwood. He then dragged the raft close to the river, taking care not to be seen. He cut the top off a plastic jug, filled it with mud from the river bank, and covered the white Styrofoam with mud in order to camouflage it. It was almost dark by the time these tasks were completed. He dug in the backpack for a bite to eat then dragged the raft to the river.

The raft was unsteady but it did float well. He made it across the river, unloaded the pack and dragged the raft up the ditch where he had been hiding the canoe on the Georgia side. One thing was sure. His means of transportation was severely diminished. Wherever he traveled now he would walk. He had no motorcycle and no canoe. When he made it back to the hill in the beaver ponds he realized he had forgotten to turn on the mobile phone at 6:00.

CHAPTER XIV

A week after his initial meeting with Jeff it was Monday morning again and Kim Buchwald was back in Jeff's office. Kim had successfully planted a seed in Jeff's mind about saving money. True to his word, Jeff had his insurance policies there and could give Kim figures on the amount of coverage as well as premiums.

Assuring Jeff that he could save him money Kim said, "I know you are busy, let me have your secretary make a copy of a few of the pages. When I get back to Atlanta I will be able to quote our coverage."

Jeff agreed and told the secretary to make the copies that Kim wanted. Kim made sure that he had a copy of the gun list along with cover pages of the policies. He thanked the secretary and left. He headed anxiously back to Atlanta. He was eager to quote Jeff a price on the insurance and anxious to give the G.B.I. the serial number of Jeff's Luger pistol.

Down at Jeff's old farm on the Alabama side of the river the agents had seen enough. They had established a regular pattern of people bringing dope upriver by boat and people meeting the boat and then hiding it in hay bales in the old barn. Periodically they would retrieve the hay bales and take them to drug dealers. The agents had watched them enough to know who the drug dealers were also.

It was time for the roundup. They knew that every two weeks, late Monday evening a boat made a delivery. The F.B.I. as well as authorities from Georgia and Alabama were involved in the arrests. They had two fast boats on the river with agents disguised as fishermen. One was upstream and one downstream of the landing area. They also had several men in the woods north and south of the landing as well as backup highway patrolmen standing by and a helicopter on standby at the Columbus airport in case it was needed. They all communicated by radio. As soon as the drug suppliers were arrested they had plans for local police

131

standing by with warrants for Jeff Callahan as well as a lot of drug salesmen. They had tapped Jeff's phone and knew he was involved in the drug dealing. He was consistently getting a share of the profit in return for letting the drug dealers use his property. He was also directing sales.

On Monday a nice cabin cruiser coming from downstream slowed and pulled into the usual landing area at Jeff's farm. Two men in a white pickup on shore left the truck and hurried down to the boat. As they were in the process of transferring dope from the boat to the men on shore the agents in boats swooped in at the same the agents on shore did. The men were arrested, handcuffed and transferred to patrol cars which were called in. It could not have gone better. The agents took possession of the drugs, the truck and the boat. These agents notified the policemen standing by to start serving the warrants for Jeff and the drug distributors.

When Kim Buchwald reached Atlanta he went straight to the G.B.I. office where McIntire and Slagle anxiously awaited his arrival.

"O.K. I got a list of his guns and serial numbers," Kim said as he laid the list on Slagle's desk.

Slagle hurriedly compared the numbers on the list with the Luger serial number.

"By golly it matches! This is it. We got him!"

"Just one request," said Kim. "Don't arrest him until I sell him some insurance."

"Well I'm sorry, but we can't promise that. We're going to have him arrested just as soon as they can prepare the warrant. Of course he will probably be out on bail, and maybe you can sell him some insurance then."

"When he realizes that my nosing around is what got him locked up I won't be able to sell him anything."

"Tell you what," said McIntire "let's get a subpoena for his insurance records before we get the warrant. We need the actual records anyway. That will take the pressure off Kim."

They immediately got on the phone to Bill Adams, the district attorney, and told him about the matching serial number.

"Well that's interesting," said Bill, "but you guys may have to stand in line to get him."

"What do you mean?" said Slagle.

"I just issued a warrant for his arrest for dealing drugs, but we can issue one for murder too. I don't know where this is going, but come on down. We'll get the subpoena for the insurance records ready and prepare a murder warrant too."

Tuesday morning McIntire and Slagle picked up the subpoena at the D.A.'s office in Columbus and went to Lumpkin. They didn't see Bill Adams so they didn't get a report on Jeff's arrest. At the Farm Bureau office they identified themselves as G.B.I. agents and presented the subpoena for Jeff's insurance records. They had copies made and got an affidavit signed and notarized stating that this was a true copy of the records. They asked the people in the Farm Bureau office not to mention the detective's interest in the records. On the way back to Columbus the agents stopped at the sheriff's office in Cusseta to talk to Walter Hooper. Mr. Hooper wasn't surprised to find out what the agents had learned.

"Well I know some news for you too," said Hooper. "Last night the F.B.I. got Jeff along with about 15 more of these jokers in the biggest drug bust they ever had in this area. They have Jeff in jail with all the others. I don't know if he is going to get out on bail or not. They got $800,000 in cash and eight million dollars worth of drugs. They think Jeff was the kingpin of the whole thing."

"Well I'll be damned," said Doug. "He must really be a bad ass. Well we are going to get this murder warrant for him too. I guess they can serve it on him in jail. Mr. Hooper said, "I don't think he's going to be out on bond from that murder warrant. You know, it's the local circuit judge's boy that got killed down there. When you present the evidence you have that Jeff is the one who killed his boy, I think Jeff's fate is sealed. I don't think he's going anywhere."

It was getting late in the day Tuesday by the time McIntire and Slagle reached Columbus. They spent the night in a motel rather than head back to Atlanta. The next morning found them at the District Attorney's office to sign the murder warrant. They were told that Jeff was still in jail and was supposed to go before the judge for a bond hearing today.

"I'm sure that when the judge sees this murder warrant Jeff will remain in jail," said Mr. Adams, the District Attorney.

On Tuesday, after Slagle and McIntire went by Sheriff Hooper's office the sheriff called Joe Schodskii. He told Joe about the matching serial numbers and Jeff's arrest on drug trafficking charges.

At six o'clock that evening Joe gave Pete the latest news.

"They caught the people delivering drugs by boat, and they have Jeff Callahan and a bunch of others locked up. Also the G.B.I. got access to Jeff's insurance records and the serial number of his insured Luger pistol matches the one you found. Can you meet me about 1:00 tomorrow?'

"I sure can," said Pete. "I'll be inside the gate at one. This sounds mighty good."

On Wednesday morning Pete left the beaver pond in hip boots, changed to the military jungle boots and proceeded to the rendezvous point well ahead of time. When Joe asked Pete if he needed anything, Pete told him to bring some insect repellant, a few cans of pork and beans and some Vienna sausage. Joe gave Pete the supplies he had ordered plus a few other things then he started bringing Pete up to date. He was full of good news.

"Pete, they have Jeff in jail along with a bunch of others. They busted up that drug ring we put them on. They got their boat, truck, all the dope, and they will probably confiscate Jeff's farm where the dope was hidden and sell it."

"Well that's good news," said Pete. "I've got about ten pounds of that stuff hidden down there in an ammo box. If I can ever come out of hiding I can show them where it is."

"I think you'll be able to come out soon. I told you they found his insurance records and the Luger serial number matches the gun you found. They are taking out a warrant for murder right now. None of them know about you yet. I think

134

you best stay hidden until they serve the murder warrant on him. They will no doubt keep him in jail then. After he is securely locked up you can come out. There are going to be a lot of surprised folks."

"Well I am ready to go somewhere. The temperature is hitting about 90 degrees every day now. The mosquitoes and deer flies are bad too. I was getting ready to leave here when my motorcycle burned up."

"Yeah, well don't worry. We are going to get you out of this mess soon. The district attorney is going to need to talk to all of us to get ready for Jeff's trial."

"By the way, "Pete said, somebody stole my canoe. When you are down on the river keep your eyes open for a green, twelve foot, Old Town canoe. Here is the serial number of mine if you happen to see one."

Pete handed Joe a piece of paper with the serial number on it. "Tell you what," said Joe. "Let me see that cell phone. I'll plug it in here in the truck and charge the battery the rest of the day. This evening I will leave it under our message rock."

"O.K., I'll just hang around this area until you bring it back."

Joe went to Sheriff Hooper's office and found out that the murder warrant had been served on Jeff Callahan. Bail had been denied. Some of the drug dealers had been able to post bond, but some had not. They called Slagle and McIntire in Atlanta and told them the news about Jeff's arrest.

Hooper told Slagle, "We need to have another meeting here with the D.A. to get our ducks in a row. We don't want any chance of Jeff's lawyers being able to discount any of our evidence."

"Well you set it up," said Slagle, "and we will be there."

"O.K., I'll get with the D.A. and we will see what we can do. I'll let you know."

Joe went back to leave the phone with Pete. When he drove through the gate Pete was there. Joe told him about the plan for a meeting of everybody with the D.A.

"Pete, you may as well come with me now. I have an extra room upstairs at my house you can have. We'll get the word out that you are alive. We will need to come to the meeting too. I know me and you both are going to play a big part in Jeff's trial."

"That sounds good Joe, but I need to pick up some things down at my hiding place. If you could pick me up here tomorrow about dark I will have my clothes and some supplies that I would like to take with me."

"O.K. fine, I'll see you here late tomorrow."

Pete had some very mixed emotions as he headed back toward the hill in the beaver pond. This was the time he had been waiting for, however the life among natural surroundings had taken on a life of its own. He was sure there would be some things about this wild life that he would miss. It would be good to see his family again, and he had often wondered about an old girlfriend he had in Atlanta and another close to the office where he worked.

Pete busied himself trying to decide what to take. He knew he couldn't take it all. He had spent too much time initially stocking the place with everything he could imagine he would need. He decided to take clothes, guns, money and some personal items now. He could return for traps, tent, cooking utensils etc. later. He looked forward to leading an expedition from the Columbus museum to possibly excavate the mound and search for Indian artifacts. The next day he packed out two loads of stuff and waited for Joe.

Joe waited until dark to pick Pete up. They didn't want to risk someone seeing Pete too soon. Joe had told his wife his plans of course. When they reached Joe's house his wife had a good dinner prepared for them.

After dinner they got on the phone to Pete's sister and brother-in-law, Norma and Larry Edenview in Atlanta. Joe reached Norma on the phone.

"Norma, I have some news for you that may be a shock. Are you sitting down?"

"What are you talking about Joe?"

"Norma, I have Pete Lancaster here with me and he is in good shape."

There was nothing but silence on the phone for a while, then Norma said, "Joe what are you talking about? I want to believe you, but I find it real hard."

Norma turned to Larry and said, "Joe Schodski says Pete is there with him."

At this time Pete spoke up, "Norma, it's me. I am sorry I put you through what I did, but I have been working to uncover the truth about who killed Jessie Smith. We have the truth now. They've got Jeff Callahan locked up on a murder warrant so I am coming out of hiding. "Oh Pete, this all sounds too good to be true."

"I'll be up there tomorrow night. What happened to my truck?'

"We have it here," said Norma. "You come on up. We have a lot of planning to do. You probably need to talk to our lawyer, Gus Bloomdale. We still have your clothes up here. We went down there and cleaned up the company house you lived in and put those things in storage. They have someone else in your place down there."

"Yeah, Joe told me about that. "O.K., we will see you tomorrow evening, and again, I am sorry for the trouble I caused you, but as things stood I was headed to jail."

That evening Joe called his boss and told him about Pete. It took quite a while to explain all the details of how Pete fit into the picture. When his boss finally understood, Joe told him that he wanted to take a couple of days off and take Pete to Atlanta. He then called Walter Hooper and explained the situation. Walter was very pleased to say the least. He told Joe for Pete to plan to attend the strategy meeting they were planning.

CHAPTER XV

The next day Joe and Pete headed to Atlanta. They stopped in Lagrange for Pete to get a haircut and get his beard shaved. This was the first haircut and shave Pete had gotten since he went into hiding. The barber told Pete that he sure got his money's worth that time. Joe had taken a picture of Pete before the barber shop visit. He took another one afterwards and told the barber he would send him a copy. Pete knew that his sister and Larry wouldn't have known him with all that hair.

Pete was having some trouble adjusting to normal living conditions. For nine months he had been very cautious about where he went and always keeping a watch on his back side. Joe noticed Pete always glancing around to see if anyone was approaching. Pete told him that he guessed that it would just take a while for him to get back to normal.

After an emotional meeting with Norma's family they sat down to talk. Pete described in detail his experiences in hiding. He described the planning that went into his scheme.

"Well you sure had us convinced," said Norma.

"Yeah," Joe said, "we had all decided you were done for. Old Jeff Callahan thought so too. He thought he was real safe after what happened to you."

Norma called Gus Bloomdale, who had been Pete's attorney when they were preparing for trial, and requested a meeting with him the next day. She then called Lewis Everett and asked him to meet them at the lawyer's office the next day.

At that meeting Pete had to explain all over again what had happened and why he did what he did. He apologized to Lewis Everett for the inconvenience he had caused by Lewis having to put up the bond money. At the last of September after Pete would have been gone a year, Pete would have been declared legally dead and Lewis would have gotten the bond money back. The lawyer assured Lewis that after a hearing on the matter his bond money would be refunded.

Joe had to get back to work. On his way out of town he visited the G.B.I. office to see James McIntire and Doug Slagle. They had already been informed of the developments. They had talked to Sheriff Walter Hooper and everyone was meeting at the district attorney's office next Tuesday. They said word had leaked out to the newspapers too. Reporters were calling everybody wanting interviews.

Slagle said, "They have got one heck of a human interest story here. This is front page news. A big, prominent, banker is in jail for shooting the judge's son and running a drug ring. A poor forester was framed. They thought he was dead and now he is alive. Boy, it doesn't get any better than that! You better hurry home. I know the reporters are wanting to talk to you."

"Yeah, the papers will have Jeff tried before he ever goes to court. They will no doubt have to move the location of the trial. After all, it is the local judge's boy who was killed. There's no way this is going to be tried in Chattahoochee County."

A few days later Joe saw Marvin Johnson, Pete's former boss. Of course he had heard the news about Pete coming out of hiding and Callahan being arrested. It seems that everyone had heard it now. It was in the newspapers and on T.V.

"Are you guys going to give Pete his old job back?" asked Joe.

"No Joe, I'm sorry to say we have already replaced him. I am anxious to see Pete and talk to him. He called me the other night. It sure was good to hear from him again. You know, the way this thing worked out he probably did the best thing he could have done."

"Yeah, I think he did too," said Joe.

"We will have a job for him. No doubt about that. We've got several slots we could put him in. It just won't be the same job."

The following Tuesday the whole team met at Bill Adam's office. Bill Adams, the prosecuting attorney, the G.B.I. agents, Joe's boss, Pete, Joe, the sheriff, and Pete's lawyer from Atlanta, and Gus Bloomdale all attended. Jeff Callahan had already had his bond hearing before the judge. Bond had been denied so Jeff was still in jail.

139

The D.A. took depositions from Joe Schodski, Pete and the G.B.I. agents. Joe described how he had put Jeff out on that fateful night and picked him up later when Jeff told him he had lost the Luger pistol. Pete described his involvement. He came upon the boys in the road. Jessie Smith had been shot and Glen Aldrich was trying to get him in the car. Pete told how he helped get the Smith boy in the car and to the hospital. He also told the circumstances of how the pistol was found. The G.B.I. described all aspects of their investigation.

Mr. Adams, the district attorney, said, "Fellows, this looks like an airtight case against Jeff. No matter how good it looks though, you never can be sure how one of these things will turn out until the case is tried. I appreciate your cooperation and will be in touch. Jeff will be tried on the drug trafficking charge first since he was arrested on that charge first."

Pete's lawyer, Gus Bloomdale, requested a meeting with Judge Smith and the district attorney. At the hearing Pete and Lewis Everett, who had signed Pete's bond, were present. As a result of this meeting the murder charge against Pete was dropped and the bond money was returned to Lewis Everett.

In Atlanta, the G.B.I. agents felt some obligation to Kim Buchwald who had helped them obtain Jeff's insurance records. There was no hope of Kim selling insurance to Jeff Callahan now. Callahan would likely be in jail for the remainder of his life. The agents talked to their boss and they were told for Kim to submit a bill for consulting services. The State of Georgia would reimburse him for his trouble.

Time went on. Jeff's trial on drug trafficking resulted in the loss of his 1,000 acre place in Alabama where the drugs were being hidden, a $500,000 fine, and ten years in jail.

The people who had pursued the murder indictment against Jeff were not satisfied with his drug conviction. They wanted him to stand trial for murder. True to everyone's expectations, Jeff's defense lawyers applied for a change of venue. Jeff and the judge were both too well known in the Columbus area. The judge and Jeff Callahan knew each other too well also. After a hearing on the matter the murder trial was moved across the state to Savannah. The trial was scheduled for the fall session of court at the Chatham County courthouse in Savannah.

In the meantime Pete had been given a job in wood procurement by Great Southern Paper Co. He worked out of an office in Eufaula, Alabama. He was furnished a company pickup truck but had to rent an apartment. His job involved buying pulpwood for the Great Southern paper mill south of Cedar Springs, Ga. The mill used 2,000 cords of wood per day. Pete bought wood for the mill from wood yards and individual contractors within a radius of 100 miles from the mill.

The news media had played up Pete's story in a big way. He had many interviews for newspaper and magazine articles. It really stirred people's interest that a person could remain hidden and survive as Pete did. In fact the Army had interviewed him for a job teaching survival techniques to soldiers at Fort Benning. The job sounded attractive, but Pete decided to stay in his chosen field.

Pete contacted a girl he had dated previously. She was still unattached. On weekends with her help he visited the cave and the hill in the beaver pond to retrieve the supplies he had left there. He also went with the F.B.I. to retrieve the package of cocaine he had hidden in an ammo box on Jeff's place across the river in Alabama. Pete was getting used to civilization again, although he still had frequent urges to watch his back trail. He never found his canoe. The motorcycle and canoe were just part of the price he paid for being framed for murder.

In September preparations were made for the trial. Bill Adams, the prosecuting attorney, assembled his witnesses. The G.B.I. agents, Joe Schodski, Pete Lancaster, and Sheriff Walter Hooper, had all been interviewed by Jeff's defense attorneys.

Finally the day arrived. Jeff was transferred to a holding cell in the Savannah jail. The prosecuting attorney's witnesses were housed by the state in a Savannah hotel. A jury that had no knowledge of the case at hand was assembled and the trial began. Although Jeff was locked in jail when the trial wasn't in progress he was allowed to wear a suit and tie. He was escorted from the jail to the courtroom by two armed guards.

As the trial progressed with the prosecution witnesses testifying about the fateful night when Jessie Smith was killed, about finding the murder weapon, the bullet tests, etc., Jeff became more and more nervous. His lawyers were desperately trying to cast doubt on the prosecution's witnesses. It was obvious to everyone that Jeff's goose was cooked.

The most damaging evidence was Joe Schodski's testimony. He related how Jeff Callahan was instrumental in establishing the game refuge, how he put his own land into it and persuaded other large landowners to do likewise. As a result of this political influence he felt like he should be able to run the show. Joe described how Jeff had wanted him to hide on the side of the road and shoot poachers. When Joe wouldn't do it Jeff persuaded Joe to put him out and pick him up later.

It was obvious that Jeff was becoming more and more agitated as the testimony piled up against him. He already had the drug trafficking conviction which he was appealing, but he knew there wasn't much chance of overturning that. If he was convicted of murder he would be executed or spend the rest of his life in jail.

The courtroom was packed. A lot of people had a special interest in the outcome of this trial. There were a lot of Pete's relatives in attendance as well as employees of Great Southern Paper Co., personnel from the Game and Fish Commission, G.B.I. witnesses, Jeff's relatives and employees, and a lot of people from the news media.

The trial ended after a week of testimony and went to the jury. The defense had offered no defense witnesses. Jeff himself did not testify. The jury was sequestered. They reached a verdict after about two hours of deliberation.

Court was scheduled to convene at nine o'clock on Monday morning, and the word was out that the jury had reached a verdict. The usual crowd and a lot of extra spectators were there. Jeff Callahan was seated at the defense table along with two defense attorneys. A prison guard stood beside Jeff.

142

At the prosecution table Joe Schodski and two prosecuting attorneys from the district attorney's office were seated. Court was convened and the jury filed into the jury box. The judge asked the jury foreman if they had reached a verdict.

"Yes we have your honor," replied the jury foreman." The courtroom was very quiet.

"Please stand and read the verdict," said the judge. The foreman stood and said, "We the jury find the defendant guilty of murder."

At this, Jeff leaped to his feet and grabbed the pistol from the guard standing beside him. He shot the guard then whirled toward the prosecution table.

"Joe, you son-of-a-bitch, I'll kill you," he said as he fired a shot toward Joe.

Joe and the prosecution attorneys ducked. Doug Slagle, the G.B.I. witness, drew a concealed pistol and would have shot Jeff, but by now both of Jeff's defense attorneys were struggling with him for the pistol. With the pistol still in hand the pistol passed underneath Jeff's chin at the moment the gun fired. The bullet exited the top of Jeff's head and blew brains and blood on the struggling attorneys.

The courtroom erupted into pandemonium. The guard had a life threatening wound in the chest. Luckily the bullet fired toward Joe hit no one.

At any rate the trial was over.

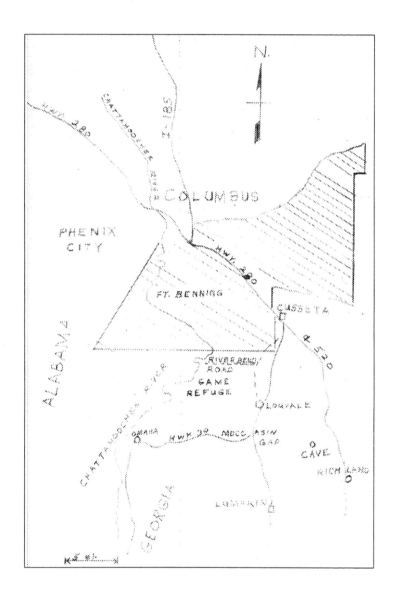